Book Two

IK

THE IRON
KINGDOM
Series

THE JERUSALEM COUNCIL

John D. Clark, Sr.

THE CONTROVERSY CONCERNING THE TWO NEW TESTAMENT GOSPELS

The Jerusalem Council
THE CONTROVERSY CONCERNING THE TWO NEW TESTAMENT GOSPELS
(The Iron Kingdom Series, Book Two)
© 2020 John David Clark, Sr.

Songs:
"Messiah Came at Last", Gary B. Savelli
"God's Son", John D. Clark, Sr.
"Jerusalem Council Hymn", John D. Clark, Sr.

ISBN-978-1-934782-32-3

Cover Design by Donna Nelson
Illustrations by Tim Sellers

Author's Notes

- In English, there is no difference in the singular and plural forms of "you". However, in biblical Hebrew and Greek, the difference is obvious. To more accurately convey the biblical writers' messages in verses where the word "you" appears, I have italicized the "y" of all plural forms, such as *y*ou, *y*our, *y*ours, *y*ourselves.

- Translations of Old and New Testament scriptures are my own. Following standard practice, when a word is added to the translation for clarification, it is italicized.

- Punctuation appears inside quotation marks only when that punctuation is part of what is quoted. To include all periods and commas within quotation marks, as many grammarians demand, leaves too much room, in my opinion, for misrepresentation of the quoted material.

For information, write to the following address:

Books – The Jerusalem Council
P. O. Box 99
Burlington, NC. 27216-0099

You can also visit us at these websites:

www.PastorJohnsHouse.com
www.GoingtoJesus.com
www.Isaiah58.com

For encouraging music all day long, go to:
www.SongsofRest.com

BOOKS OF THE BIBLE AND THEIR ABBREVIATIONS

Old Testament Books

Genesis	Gen.	Ecclesiastes	Eccl.
Exodus	Ex.	Song of Solomon	Song
Leviticus	Lev.	Isaiah	Isa.
Numbers	Num.	Jeremiah	Jer.
Deuteronomy	Dt.	Lamentations	Lam.
Joshua	Josh.	Ezekiel	Ezek.
Judges	Judg.	Daniel	Dan.
Ruth	Ruth	Hosea	Hos.
1Samuel	1Sam.	Joel	Joel
2Samuel	2Sam.	Amos	Amos
1Kings	1Kgs.	Obadiah	Obad.
2Kings	2Kgs.	Jonah	Jon.
1Chronicles	1Chron.	Micah	Mic.
2Chronicles	2Chron.	Nahum	Nah.
Ezra	Ezra	Habakkuk	Hab.
Nehemiah	Neh.	Zephaniah	Zeph.
Esther	Esth.	Haggai	Hag.
Job	Job	Zechariah	Zech.
Psalms	Ps.	Malachi	Mal.
Proverbs	Prov.		

New Testament Books

Matthew	Mt.	1Timothy	1Tim.
Mark	Mk.	2Timothy	2Tim.
Luke	Lk.	Titus	Tit.
John	Jn.	Philemon	Phlm.
Acts	Acts	Hebrews	Heb.
Romans	Rom.	James	Jas.
1Corinthians	1Cor.	1Peter	1Pet.
2Corinthians	2Cor.	2Peter	2Pet.
Galatians	Gal.	1John	1Jn.
Ephesians	Eph.	2John	2Jn.
Philippians	Phip.	3John	3Jn.
Colossians	Col.	Jude	Jude
1Thessalonians	1Thess.	Revelation	Rev.
2Thessalonians	2Thess.		

Contents

Foreword. . . . . *xi*

Introduction. . . . . *xiii*

Characters. . . . . *xix*

Part 1: The Council Begins 5

Part 2: Paul Explains and Defends His Gospel 29

Part 3: Paul Declares that Moses' Law Will End. 77

Part 4: The Council Concludes 151

Part 5: The Apostasy of the Body of Christ. 169

Afterword. 189

Foreword

I believe the Bible. I trust it to be historically and prophetically true. I believe that Jesus is Lord, that he was born of the virgin Mary, that he suffered and died for our sins, that on the third day, he was raised from the dead by the power of God, that he ascended into heaven to offer himself to God for our sins, that he will return at the appointed time to reign on earth a thousand years, and that in the Final Judgment, he will be the Judge of both the living and the dead. I believe that there is no hope of salvation except by faith in Jesus Christ, God's Son. Jesus has filled me with his Spirit and taught me. I am his servant.

I also believe that the religious system known as Christianity is an abomination to both God and Jesus. I believe that, to date, Christianity is Satan's crowning achievement, and that by it, he has successfully divided and confused the body of Christ, and that he reigns over the flock of God through Christian ministers. And I believe that in order for God's people to attain to the unity and purity that Jesus prayed they would enjoy, they must come out of the religious system known as Christianity.

I am, by the wonderful grace of God, a follower of Jesus. I am also, by that same grace, not a Christian and not a part of what you know as Church religion.

The Iron Kingdom Series, of which this book is the second part, is an explanation and defense of my faith.

Introduction

What you are about to read is not fiction. It is an attempt to communicate the issues debated among the believers who took part in the Jerusalem Council of Acts 15. Though the actual words spoken are unknown, and some of the character names imagined, the substance of their arguments is Biblically accurate. There really were devout believers in the beginning of this New Testament era who argued vehemently against Paul's gospel at the Jerusalem Council. We can deduce what their arguments were, and we know what responses Paul and others gave them, from what is found in the Bible, as is evidenced by the 400-plus scriptural references that are included. Indeed, if I had included all possible references from our New Testament books, there would be many more references than that. I decided not to use references to books written by the apostles after the Jerusalem Council because at the time of the Council, those books did not exist and would have borne no weight in argument.

The apostle Paul gave names to the two gospels found in the New Testament; the one for the Jews he called "the Gospel of the Circumcision", and the one for the Gentiles, "the Gospel of the Uncircumcision". The first gospel, Paul said, was committed to Peter, and the second was committed to him (Gal. 2:7). Others besides Peter could preach the gospel for the Jews, of course, and others besides Paul could preach the gospel for the Gentiles, but Peter was the most prominent preacher of the one, and Paul, the most prominent of the other.

The two gospels were identical, except for one point: the law. Peter's gospel for the Jews required it, but Paul's gospel for the Gentiles did not. It could be argued that the two gospels were but two versions of the same gospel; however, that single difference between them was of such importance that Paul uttered a curse on the Jewish teachers who taught the Gospel of the Circumcision to his Gentile converts (Gal. 1:8–9).[1] He even wished that God would damn them (Gal. 5:12). It is important to understand that the "perverted" gospel which Paul said those teachers taught (Gal. 1:7) was actually the true gospel when it was preached to the right people, that is, to the Jews. What made it false was only its being taught to the Gentiles.

---

[1] Since God never sent Peter's gospel to the Gentiles, it can be argued that it was not really Peter's gospel that those men were teaching, but a gospel of their own imagination.

The validity of Paul's gospel was the most contentious issue among first- and second-generation believers. They just could not come to an agreement as to whether or not God had intended all along for the law of Moses to come to an end, as Paul taught. Peter and the other apostles acknowledged Paul's ordination by God to preach a different gospel, and they respected the boundaries of their respective gospels. However, their acknowledgement of Paul's gospel for the Gentiles did not settle the issue for many Jewish teachers and believers, and the more zealous of them went to the Gentiles anyway, carrying Peter's gospel and slandering Paul. They did not believe that God had revealed to Paul a gospel which excluded the law. The pattern was the same almost everywhere: Paul would establish Gentile congregations in the faith of Jesus, and then at some point afterward, he would find himself having to fight again for his Gentile converts against Jewish teachers who were leading them to submit to the ceremonial forms of Moses' law.

It is a mistake to assume that the Jerusalem Assembly's acknowledgement of Paul's Gospel settled the matter for the Assemblies of God everywhere. The letter which James and the elders wrote at the conclusion of the Council to the Assembly in Antioch did nothing to change the minds of many Jewish believers. Most Jews outside of Jerusalem and Antioch would never have even seen a copy of it, and mere rumors of the letter would not have borne sufficient weight to persuade believers of its meaning or authority. The same may also be said of believing Gentiles, and Paul spent the rest of his life struggling to save his Gentile converts from the onslaught of men who taught Peter's gospel to them. Throughout the New Testament, we see Paul pleading with the saints to put all their trust in Christ Jesus and to refuse the temptation to add ceremony to their faith.

Paul, unable to be everywhere at once, could not put out the multitude of fires that were burning the knowledge of the truth out of the hearts of his Gentile converts, and after the first-century Gentile Assemblies rejected Paul's gospel in favor of Peter's, it was just a matter of time before the entire body of Christ degenerated into just another worldly organization. The more time that passed, the more ceremonial form was added, and the more that ceremonial form was added, the more worldly the body of Christ became. In the end, in spite of the monumental efforts of Paul, the doctrine which held that all believers, Jew and Gentile, should be ceremonially as well as spiritually clean won the day (cp. 2Tim. 1:15). And spiritually speaking, it is still winning. The fact that Paul lost his battle to establish the Gentiles in the faith which Christ Jesus had revealed to him for them means, as it has meant since the last days of the apostles, that when one is invited to believe the Gospel that Paul preached, he is being invited to join the losing side in the warfare for the hearts of most believers.

Our hope is to make the Reader aware of the issue at the heart of this controversy, which is, the unique authority of Christ Jesus to save. That, as simple and innocuous as it sounds, was the most divisive doctrinal issue of the first century for the body of Christ, and, it is as much resisted by the body of Christ today as it was then. If you are a good Christian, my Reader, I am confident that, without realizing it, and like the Jewish brothers who opposed Paul at the Jerusalem Council, you, too, would oppose that truth if its meaning were to be explained to you. My hope is that when you read this Jerusalem Council, your eyes will be opened to the incomparable glory of God revealed in the eternal gospel which Jesus gave to his servant Paul.

THE
JERUSALEM
COUNCIL

John D. Clark, Sr.

THE CONTROVERSY CONCERNING
THE TWO NEW TESTAMENT GOSPELS

Characters

__Narrator__
__Scribe__
__Elders (6)__

Jacobus [*Jesus' brother*]	early 50s. leader of the Council.
Daniel [*had been w/ Jesus*]	60-ish. wise, slow to speak, from Nazareth.
Joseph [*had been w/ Jesus*]	early 70s. respected, loving, not learned.
Nahum [*had been w/ Jesus*]	early 70s. experienced, calm, and meek.
Nicodemus [*met with Jesus*]	mid-60s. simple, sincere.
Jared [*had been w/ Jesus*]	mid-50s. knowledgeable, cautious, not for Paul.

__Apostles (9)__

Barnabas, Paul, John, Andrew, Philip, Matthew, Bartholomew, Simon Peter, Cleopas

__Peter's Companions (6)__

Elkanah, Kenaz, Ahijah, Azariah, Eliezar, Joel

__Pharisees (4)__

Hananiah [*had been w/ Jesus. went to Antioch*] early 50s. learned, sincere, clings to the law, an old friend of Barnabas.
Benjamin [*protege of Hananiah*] mid-20's. analytical, humble, close to Andrew.

Micah [*had been w/ Jesus.*]	50-ish. learned, sincere, clings to the law.
Maschil [*protege of Micah*]	late-20s. perceptive, sincere.

__Scribes (2)__

Uzziel [*had been w/ Jesus*]	mid-50s. learned, perceptive, opposes Paul.
Levi [*protege of Uzziel*]	30-ish. strongly anti-Paul.

__Other Brothers (6)__

Silas [*had been w/ Jesus*]	mid-40s. wise, reasonable, believes Paul and Barnabas.
Simeon	40-ish. inclined to high-sounding cliches.
Nathan	30-ish. quiet, conciliatory, looks for something all can agree on.
Nadab	mid-30s. a mediocre mind and spirit, opposes Paul and Barnabas.
Hilkiah	mid-30s. tries to be reasonable, but is skeptical.
Eli	40-ish. angry, despises Paul's new gospel.

__The brothers who went to Antioch with Hananiah (3)__

Hillel [*had been w/ Jesus*]	60-ish. learned, bitterly opposes Paul and Barnabas.
Hushai	mid-30s. zealous, sarcastic, bitterly opposes Paul and Barnabas.
Lamech [*had been w/ Jesus. former protege of Daniel*]	late-40s. knowledgeable, crafty, bitterly opposes Paul and Barnabas.

PART 1

THE COUNCIL BEGINS

———❦———

The Reason for the Council

Narrator: The Council that is mentioned in Acts 15 was called by the apostles and elders in Jerusalem in order to deal with a controversy which arose after some men from the Jerusalem Assembly traveled to Antioch, where Barnabas and Paul were ministering. When those men arrived in Antioch and found believing Gentiles in that Assembly who had not received circumcision, they warned those Gentiles that unless they were circumcised according to the custom of Moses, that is, unless they converted to the Jewish religion,[2] they would not be saved from the coming wrath of God.[3] Barnabas and Paul vehemently opposed them, but the leaders of the Antiochan Assembly, unable to determine who was right, sent a few of their number with Paul and Barnabas to Jerusalem to present the matter to the apostles and elders. There, Paul and Barnabas testified to the whole Assembly that God had been using them to convert Gentiles to Christ without requiring them to become Jews. However, Pharisees in the Jerusalem Assembly objected to their testimony, insisting that the brothers who had gone to Antioch were right and that Gentiles who believed must be circumcised and keep Moses' law.[4] The apostles and elders then called a special Council apart from the Assembly to discuss the matter.[5]

Those in this Council who argued against Barnabas and Paul were devout men, filled with the Spirit, and expert in the scriptures; indeed, had

---

[2] The goal of circumcision was not merely to be circumcised. Circumcision was the door through which one passed to enter into the covenant God made with Israel at Mount Sinai, thereby to take on the responsibilities (and receive the blessings) of an Israelite (cf. Ex. 12:48). Paul made this clear when he cautioned Gentile believers that if they received circumcision, they were "obligated to keep the entire law" (Gal. 5:3).

[3] Acts 15:1.

[4] Acts 15:4–5. I have imagined that the men who went to Antioch and troubled the Gentiles participated in this meeting, but the Bible does not say so.

[5] In Galatians 2:1–10, Paul refers to a private meeting with the elders and apostles in Jerusalem which took place at least seventeen years after his conversion (cf. Gal. 1:18–24; 2:1), which, in turn, took place some years after the Spirit first came. The similarities between the meetings described in Galatians 2 and Acts 15 are enough to warrant the assumption that they are the same meeting.

they not been such men, they would not have been allowed to participate in this meeting. In arguing their point, they made frequent and skillful use of Scripture, and they especially emphasized the fact that Jesus himself kept the law and that all the apostles and elders were still keeping it. Paul and Barnabas, on the other hand, based their case on a revelation they had received from Jesus of a gospel for Gentiles that did not include Moses' law, though they acknowledged that God still required Jewish believers to keep it. Their opponents, though, demanded that *all* believers must submit to the law or be damned.

We are given almost no details of the arguments made in the Jerusalem Council, but we are told that there was "much disputing," just as there had been "no small dissension and debate" in Antioch. What is certain is that knowledgable, Spirit-filled men stood in both camps, and arguments on both sides were powerful and persuasive. Feelings ran deep, and zeal was lacking on neither side, for, as both sides fully understood, the direction of the body of Christ on earth was at stake, and, as both sides believed, souls were hanging in the balance. Knowing the essential points which the debaters would have made, I humbly suggest the following version of this important Council, called by the apostles and elders of the Assembly of God in Jerusalem to deal with the most important issue that first century believers faced.

————

Jacobus Opens the Council

Jacobus: Men and brothers, I greet you today in the name of Messiah Jesus. May God be with us in this meeting.

Council members: *Amen! Etc.*[6] *[Someone begins to sing a hymn. Everyone joins in.]*[7]

> Let our God, the God of Israel, surround us,
>   for His Son, our holy Shepherd, came and found us!
> To the people He has chosen, let His kingdom come!
>   Let our God, the God of Israel, now crown us!
>
> Let His chosen people Israel now hear Him.
>   Let them join in singing Zion's song and fear Him!
> At the Father's invitation, we approach His sacred throne.
>   Let His chosen people, Israel, draw near Him!

---

[6] Comments and noises from Council members are heard throughout. There was no strictly enforced order.

[7] "Jerusalem Council Hymn" by John D. Clark, Sr.

Let the nations of the earth come and adore Him,
>so that they might know the mercy waiting for them!
Let them tremble at His power! Let them bless His holy name,
>and with gifts and sacrifices fall before Him!

Jacobus Presents the Issue to the Council

Jacobus: Now, brothers, unity among those who believe in Messiah Jesus is of such importance that it occupied Messiah's thoughts in the last hours of his life here, and he took precious time from his few remaining hours to earnestly pray for it.[8] By this, we know that our unity is one of his deepest desires.

John: Yes, and the Lord also promised that if we were united, he would be with us. He told us, "Where two or three are gathered together in my name, I am there, in the midst of them."[9]

Council members: *Amen! Etc.*

Nahum:[10] May God make it so with us today!

Council members: *Amen! Etc.*

Jacobus: David the king informed us that unity in the family of God is not merely sweet, but that it also carries with it great blessing and an authority equal to that of the high priest himself [11] – a blessing certainly to be desired!

Council members: *Amen! Etc.*

Jacobus: And so, we are gathered today to resolve an issue that threatens to divide us. For not long ago, Hananiah went to Antioch with Hushai and Lamech to visit the Assembly there. When they arrived, they found Gentiles in that Assembly who believed in Messiah but had not been circumcised according to the custom of the law. So, these brothers warned those Gentiles that unless they submitted to circumcision and became part of our nation, they would not be saved with Israel when Jesus returns, but would suffer the wrath of God along with all the heathen. Now, when Barnabas and Paul heard them teaching this, they stopped them, saying they had no authority to command such things of Gentiles who believe. Upon that, a great controversy arose, and when, after much disputing, the elders of Antioch could not resolve the matter, the Assembly

---

[8] Jn. 17:11b, 20–23.

[9] Mt. 18:20.

[10] Since the Bible does not name all the participants in this Council, I have given names to many of them.

[11] Ps. 133:1–2.

there decided to send Barnabas and Paul with a few of their elders here, to present the issue to us. And they are most welcome.

Council members: *Amen! Etc.*

Nahum: And we welcome as well the young man of the Gentiles whom Barnabas and Paul brought with them. What is his name again?

Paul: It is Titus, sir.

Nahum: Yes, yes, I remember now. Welcome, Titus!

Council members: *Amen! Etc.*

Jacobus: Amen. Welcome to you all.

Now, men and brothers, as you know, after Barnabas and Paul arrived the other day, they testified in our Assembly that God had wrought mighty works among the Gentiles by their hands and that many Gentiles had believed but were not afterward circumcised. Then some of us rose up and joined with these brothers in opposing Barnabas and Paul, testifying that all who believe in Messiah Jesus must be circumcised and keep the law if they hoped to be spared the coming wrath.

We have at no time experienced division such as this since the day God poured out His Spirit from on high, and when we elders saw that the congregation was troubled by the dissension, we decided to consider the issue in private, apart from the full Assembly, and we have gathered today for that purpose. So, I propose that we hear first from Barnabas and Paul, and then from Hananiah and anyone else who has something to say concerning their new doctrine. And may God resolve this controversy and rid us of the turmoil which has arisen because of it.

Council members: *Amen! Etc.*

Jacobus: I will sit now, and we will hear you all. Speak freely, and God will make His judgment known. [*Jacobus sits.*]

Council members: *Amen! Etc.*

Barnabas Argues His Case

Barnabas: [*Barnabas rises.*] Men and brothers, Paul has asked me to speak first, since I am so well acquainted with you all, men whom I have loved since I sold my possessions and forsook my island home to come here, determined to devote myself with you all to the gospel of God.[12]

Council members: *Amen! Etc.*

Barnabas: We live in an extraordinary time, brothers, for even though God commanded us by the hand of Moses not to add anything to the

---

[12] Acts 4:36–37.

law,[13] God Himself has added His Son, to redeem for Himself a people from Israel, as the prophet said, "A Redeemer is coming to Zion, even to those in Jacob who repent of their transgression."[14]

Council members: *Amen! Etc.*

Barnabas: As you know, following the persecution which arose throughout Judea after the stoning of Stephen, some fled these parts and went to Antioch, where they preached the gospel, but only to the Jews, as was proper at that time.[15] However, some who fled to Antioch were not originally from Judea, but from Cyrene and Cyprus, and in time past, they had been conversant with Gentiles. There, in the normal course of life, they spoke of Messiah to the Gentiles they met, many of whom received their testimony and believed. And when we in Jerusalem heard of that, we were glad, and you chose me to go to Antioch to exhort and encourage them all, which I gladly did. And after I arrived, the Lord gave a great increase to the Assembly there.

Later, when I heard that Paul was again in his hometown of Tarsus in Cilicia, I went to Tarsus and brought him back with me to Antioch to help me in the work.[16] I believed that since Paul himself was a Roman citizen,[17] he would be of help to me in understanding and dealing with the Gentiles, and my expectation of help was not in vain.

Now, just prior to that, here in Judea, you will remember that God sent Simon Peter to Caesarea to preach in the house of a Gentile, Cornelius by name, a Roman centurion who feared our God and had done much good for our people.[18] And when Simon arrived at Cornelius' house and began to preach, the Spirit suddenly fell upon Cornelius and the others in his house, none of whom were circumcised. And if you will remember, brothers, when Simon returned to Jerusalem and reported what had happened, many of you here today, and in this same room, were indignant against Simon because entering a Gentile's house was not only contrary to our tradition, but it was also contrary to the prohibition that Jesus once gave to you who were his disciples.[19]

Apostles: *Yes. That is true. I remember. Etc.*

---

[13] Dt. 12:32.

[14] Isa. 59:20.

[15] Acts 11:19.

[16] Acts 11:20–26.

[17] Acts 22:25–28.

[18] The story of Cornelius is found in Acts 10.

[19] Mt. 10:1–5.

Barnabas: Consequently, you elders rebuked Simon for going to a Gentile's house. Do you remember?

Jacobus, Joseph, Nahum, Silas: *Yes, we remember. Etc.*

Barnabas: It struck me then, as I know it did you, how humbly and patiently Simon explained to us that God had given him an astonishing vision and had commanded him to go to Caesarea with the messengers Cornelius had sent to find him. Then Simon told us that after he entered the house of Cornelius, when he had just begun to preach, God poured out His Spirit on those uncircumcised Gentiles, just as He had poured it out on you all in the beginning.[20]

Council members: *Yes. I remember. Etc.*

Barnabas: And you may also remember that Simon concluded his account by asking a question that no one here could answer.

Joseph: How well do I remember, Barnabas! Simon asked us, "Who was I, that I could withstand God?"[21]

Barnabas: And only then did you elders relent, when you could not answer that question.

Joseph: Yes, we were convinced by then that God had indeed given His Spirit to Gentiles, as unbelievable as that seemed to us at the time. So, we had no choice but to believe Simon.

Council members: *That is true. Amen. Etc.*

Silas: Yes, Simon's testimony compelled us all to acknowledge that God had granted His Spirit to those Gentiles, just as He had granted it to us Jews in the beginning.

Barnabas: Now, brothers, I admit that I followed you in opposing what Simon had done, but we opposed him because we were ignorant. We did not expect God to ever give His holy Spirit to the heathen, and we did not know how to justify what had happened, for it was contrary to the gospel which Jesus himself preached and which we all still preach to the Jews.

Council members: *Comments.*

Barnabas: But the doctrine we lacked then, the doctrine which would explain what God did at the house of Cornelius has now been revealed, and God has sent Paul and me to the Gentiles with it. For one day, after I had brought Paul to Antioch, as the Assembly worshipped, the Spirit spoke and commanded them, saying, "Set Barnabas and Paul apart for me, for the work to which I have called them!" And so, after the congregation

---

[20] Acts 11:15.

[21] Acts 11:17–18.

fasted and prayed, they laid their hands on us and sent us on our way.[22] Therefore, to the Gentiles we go, carrying the message which Cornelius and his house heard from Simon before God interrupted his sermon and filled them with the Spirit.

Micah: Interrupted him?

Barnabas: Yes. Simon, didn't you tell us that you had just begun to speak when the Spirit fell on those Gentiles?

Simon Peter: Yes.[23] I intended to preach to Cornelius the gospel I had been preaching from the beginning.

Philip: . . . the gospel we *all* had been preaching.

Simon Peter: Yes, that they should repent and receive John's baptism, that is, be baptized in the name of Jesus, so that they might then receive the Spirit.[24]

Barnabas: But God finished your sermon for you, for when those Gentiles had heard all that God wanted them to hear, He poured out His Spirit on them before you preached the gospel that you had always preached, the gospel that Jesus had given all of you to preach.

Simon Peter: That's true, Barnabas.

Barnabas: And the message those Gentiles heard from Simon is the message Jesus has now sent Paul and me to preach to the Gentiles, which is, if Gentiles do righteous deeds and believe in Jesus, God will grant them remission of sins *without submission to Moses' law*. And that is precisely what He did to Cornelius and his house.

Council members: *Comments*.

Barnabas: Ask yourselves this question, brothers. If God requires believing Gentiles to be circumcised and keep the law, then why did He interrupt Simon's sermon and prevent him from telling those Gentiles about circumcision and the law? Was God in a hurry? You have heard the old saying, "Holiness in a hurry is a highway to hell."[25] So, did He err in His excitement and make a mistake?

Uzziel: Now, wait. God is never hasty.

Barnabas: That is my point.

Uzziel: I have a question.

Nahum: In time, brother Uzziel. Let us finish this first.

Uzziel: Very well.

---

[22] Acts 13:1–3.

[23] Acts 11:15.

[24] Acts 2:38.

[25] Cf. Prov. 19:2.

Barnabas: Simon, some of these men with us today have not heard from your lips how it happened.

Simon Peter: No, I suppose not. Well, God's angel had appeared to Cornelius and told him that his righteous deeds had risen as a memorial before God and that he should send for me at Joppa. Then, after the servants of Cornelius came and brought me to Cornelius' house, I began to preach, telling them that if they believed in Jesus, God would grant them remission of sins. They must have believed me, for it was at that very moment, when I mentioned the words, "remission of sins", that God poured out His Spirit on them, and their sins were remitted.

Council members: *Comments.*

Barnabas: That is because they had worked righteousness in the sight of God before you came. And after you came, they believed in Jesus, and those are the only two things that God requires of the Gentiles!

Council members: *Comments.*

Barnabas: And now, God has sent Paul and me to preach that message, and in obedience to His command, we have traveled to many cities, declaring to the Gentiles that a door to the kingdom of the living God is now open for them and that they should repent and believe the gospel. And those who do so are precious saints of God.

Jesus said that whoever forsook family and houses and lands for his sake would receive a hundredfold now, in this life,[26] and Paul and I have found that to be true as we preached in the foreign lands to which Jesus sent us. In almost every place we traveled, we found some who believed our preaching, and those who believed joyfully opened up their homes and their lives to us, just as you all did to me when I first came here from Crete. I do not exaggerate when I say that among some of them, their love for us and the gospel was so great that they would have plucked out their eyes for us, had we needed them.

Men and brothers, God has set His seal upon our gospel for the Gentiles many times by baptizing with His Spirit precious souls among the Gentiles who believed our preaching and repented of their sins, though they did not know the law. So, I will ask you now, as Simon once asked us, "Who are we, that we should withstand God?"

Council members: *Comments.*

Barnabas: This is why, when Hananiah and the others arrived in Antioch and demanded of the Gentiles things which God does not demand, Paul and I contended with them. The elders in Antioch had been content with our gospel, but being inexpert in the scriptures, they became

---

[26] Mk. 10:30.

confused when these brothers condemned it. And because they did not know what was right, they sent us here with faithful men from that Assembly, so that you apostles and elders might confirm for them the truth of our gospel. [*Barnabas sits.*]

Council members: *Comments.*

Jacobus: Thank you, Barnabas. And again, we greet the elders who have come with you from Antioch, and brother Titus. I believe that God will give them the assurance they desire.

Council members: *Amen. Etc.*

Jacobus: Now, Hananiah, what have you to say?

Hananiah Argues His Case

Hananiah: Uzziel, you had a question?

Uzziel: No, I will wait. I want to hear you.

Hananiah: As you wish. [*Hananiah rises.*] First of all, Jacobus, I join you in hope that God will restore the unity which His Assemblies enjoyed before the advent of this new doctrine. My hope is that God will purify His Assemblies so that we may once again be blessed together in the sweet unity of the one true faith, according to the promise of God: "I will give them one heart and one way, that they might fear me always, for their good and for the good of their children after them."[27] I give God thanks for the wise elders we have here, men loved by God and by all the upright. And we are also thankful that God has kept my dear brother Barnabas safe while he was away from us and that He has returned him to us in good health.

Council members: *Amen. Etc.*

Hananiah: Now, as we would expect, my friend Barnabas has said much that is true. We do indeed live in an extraordinary time, just as he said, for God has fulfilled His promise to our fathers to send the Redeemer, our Lord Jesus, to Israel. And we eagerly await the return of Messiah Jesus to fulfill the remaining promises and to reign over the earth forever from this holy city!

Council members: *Amen! Praise God! Etc.*

Hananiah: Men and brothers, I am not blind. I know that most of you have already given your assent to this gospel of Barnabas and Paul. Some of you have told me so. But I pray you, as just men, to hear me out, for I cannot believe that in assenting to their gospel, you have considered the matter as fully as you might have. We must be circumspect in our judg-

---

[27] Jer. 32:39.

ments, brothers. Wise Solomon understood that the man who presents his case first always seems right,[28] and he warned us not to make judgments before thoroughly considering an issue. He said, "It is folly and shame to him who responds to a matter before hearing it out."[29] So, I am grateful for the opportunity to present the other side of this matter.

To begin, I must re-emphasize something that has already been mentioned, but may not have been sufficiently considered, to wit, the household of God has not suffered division over doctrine since the time Messiah walked among us, but has been faithful to the gospel he preached. We have suffered through persecutions together and have overcome other challenges to our faith, but the faith itself has never been a matter of controversy because we all believed what Jesus taught us. Our faith, the faith of Messiah Jesus, is sound; it is sure; and it has brought us very great blessings.

Council members: *Amen. That is true. Etc.*

Hananiah: Even when Ananias and his wife were slain by the Lord for their attempt to deceive the Spirit, it was not a doctrinal matter, but a moral failure which cost them their lives. So, I would ask that every man here take special note of the undeniable fact that the Assemblies of God suffered no division concerning the faith until the introduction of this new doctrine. That is significant because, as brother Jacobus rightly said, it is Messiah's fervent desire that all who believe in him work and worship together in perfect unity. I have thought much lately about how pleased he and the Father must have been these past two decades to see our unity as we strove together for the gospel that Messiah taught us. But where is that precious unity now, brothers? And what has brought on this confusion?

Micah: Excellent question, Hananiah.

Council members: *Comments.*

Hananiah: Brothers, all of us who know Barnabas know him to be a good and faithful man.

Council members: *Amen. That is right! Etc.*

Hananiah: He is also an astute man and an accomplished speaker, and he can be very persuasive. But again, I caution you, my friends, to guard your hearts above all else, as Solomon warned us,[30] lest you be swept up in excellent speech and fail to examine carefully the words that have been spoken. False words can sound true. I admit that Barnabas sounds right,

---

[28] Prov. 18:17.
[29] Prov. 18:13.
[30] Prov. 4:23.

but good men can have wrong ideas, and good men who are adept with words can make wrong ideas sound right.

Council members: *Comments.*

Hananiah: Ahithophel, King David's wisest counsellor, was also a good man. His counsel was like an oracle of God.[31] However, wrong thoughts turned his heart against David, and he gave his cunning counsel to Prince Absalom instead, which led Absalom to commit irreversible outrage against his father.[32] Our history contains many such stories, and they teach us that the ideas most destructive to our nation have been those promulgated by good men gone astray.

Council members: *Comments.*

Hananiah: But to give more specific answer to our brother Barnabas, I deny his assertion that we who traveled to Antioch demanded of the Gentiles what God does not demand. Every prophet who ever prophesied of these last days spoke of the Gentiles coming to Israel and submitting to God's law. Zechariah said, "Many people will come, even mighty nations, to seek the LORD of Hosts in Jerusalem and to entreat the LORD's favor."[33] Isaiah said, "The foreigner will join himself to them and be united with the house of Jacob."[34] And Ezekiel said that Messiah Jesus will welcome the heathen who come to Israel and will command us Jews to "divide this land among *y*ou and the foreigner who sojourns among *y*ou. They shall be to *y*ou as native sons of Israel; along with *y*ou, they shall be divided an inheritance among the tribes of Israel."[35] How many such prophecies there are! Jeremiah said, "O LORD, to you will come nations from the farthest reaches of earth, and they will say, 'Our fathers inherited nothing but falsehood and vanity.'"[36] There is no prophet who contradicts these things, brothers. They all agree, for the same God spoke through them all.

Uzziel, Hillel, Levi, Hilkiah, Eli, Hushai, Lamech, Benjamin, Micah, Maschil, Nadab: *Amen! Etc.*

Hananiah: Isaiah even spoke of the Gentiles coming to this land to be our servants! "Strangers will stand and tend *y*our flocks, and the children of foreigners will be *y*our plowmen and *y*our vinedressers."[37] And again,

---

[31] 2Sam. 16:23.

[32] 2Sam. 16:21–22.

[33] Zech. 8:22–23.

[34] Isa. 14:1b.

[35] Ezek. 47:21–23.

[36] Jer. 16:19.

[37] Isa. 61:5.

"Sons of the foreigner will build your wall, and their kings will serve you."[38] And again, "They will bow before you, face to the earth, and lick the dust of your feet."[39] "They will follow you in chains. They will pass over and bow down to you. They will entreat you, *saying*, 'God is with you, and there is no other God! No other!'"[40] "Nations will come to your light, and kings to the brightness of your rising."[41] And "at that time, they will call Jerusalem, 'the throne of the LORD', and all the nations will be gathered to it, to Jerusalem, to the name of the LORD, and they will no longer walk after the stubbornness of their evil heart."[42]

Council members: *Comments.*

Hananiah: But note especially, brothers, that the Gentiles will not be coming to this land expecting to remain Gentiles and continue in their ways, but to join us in serving God under the law! For both Isaiah and Micah said, "Many nations will go, and they will say, 'Come, and let us go up to the mountain of Jehovah, even to the house of the God of Jacob! And He will teach us of His ways, and we will walk in His paths.' For from Zion will the law go forth, and the word of the LORD from Jerusalem.'"[43] And we all know that when God repeats a thing, it is certain, just as Joseph once told Pharaoh.[44]

Council members: *Comments.*

Hananiah: I assure you, brothers, that neither I nor these men who went with me to Antioch have anything against the Gentiles who believe; on the contrary, we love them and we welcome them! As does God, so do we!

Hillel: That is the reason we went to Antioch in the first place, to welcome them into our fellowship. Let the Gentiles believe in Messiah Jesus! We rejoice in that. But let them not ignore our law, for they cannot be saved without it! Only those who worship God according to His will worship God rightly, and His will was revealed in Moses and the prophets as well as in Jesus.

Hushai: Yes, let the Gentiles come – but as the prophets said they should, not in their uncircumcised filthiness! We will gladly welcome them.

---

[38] Isa. 60:10a.

[39] Isa. 49:23a.

[40] Isa. 45:14b.

[41] Isa. 60:3.

[42] Jer. 3:17.

[43] Mic. 4:1–2; Isa. 2:3.

[44] Gen. 41:32.

Nadab: By all means, let them come in!

Nathan: We earnestly desire it.   By all means, let us serve God together.

Council members: *Comments.*

Joseph: Patience, brothers. Let Hananiah finish.

Hananiah: We know that the uncircumcised Gentiles to whom God sent Simon Peter some years ago were ignorant of our law when God poured out His Spirit on them.   But it appears that a great error in judgment has been made by some of you concerning that astonishing event, for you seem to have mistaken God's compassion for those ignorant Gentiles to be a sanctioning of their uncircumcised ways.

You will recall that in King Hezekiah's day, some Israelites, as ignorant of the law as were Cornelius and his house, came to Jerusalem to keep the Passover but were unprepared according to the law.   And you will recall that when Hezekiah prayed for God's indulgence, God heard the King's prayer and not only forgave their error, but even healed them.[45] But did that great mercy from God, contrary to the law as it was, mean that God no longer required obedience to His law? Of course not. Those ignorant Israelites of Hezekiah's day were expected to know the law when the next feast came around; otherwise, God would have cursed them. God is good, but He is nobody's fool.

Council members: *Comments.*

Hananiah: You will also recall that David, out of dire necessity, once transgressed the law in order to feed himself and his starving men, taking and eating sanctified bread which only the priests are permitted to eat. But again, God overlooked that transgression, forgave David and his men, and spared their lives. So, I ask you, was God, in showing such mercy, giving permission for men to come and eat the holy bread whenever they wished?

Council members: *Comments.*

Hananiah: Of course not! Had David come to the sanctuary when his belly was full and eaten one crumb of the holy bread, it would have been an unforgivable transgression.

Council members: *Comments.*

Hananiah: So, yes, God gave His Spirit to the uncircumcised at Cornelius' house, but He expected us to rejoice at His mercy on the heathen, not to devise a new doctrine that teaches them that they need not obey God's law! God will accept the worship of the Gentiles just as He accepts ours, and He will bless them just as He blesses us, *when they*

---

[45] 2Chron. 30:17–20.

serve God just as we serve Him. The prophet Isaiah said, "As for the children of the foreigner who join themselves to the LORD, every one who keeps my Sabbath rather than profane it and who holds fast my covenant, them will I bring to my holy mountain and make joyful in my house of prayer. Their burnt offerings and their sacrifices will be acceptable on my altar, for my house will be called a house of prayer for all peoples."[46] No man said these things, brothers; God did! He said as plainly as it can be said that He will accept the worship of the heathen *if they keep His Sabbath and His law!*

Uzziel, Hillel, Levi, Hilkiah, Eli, Hushai, Lamech, Benjamin, Micah, Maschil, Nadab: *Amen! Etc.*

Hananiah: These sayings are true and worthy of acceptance by all. And these prophecies must come to pass, for as Messiah Jesus said, "The scriptures cannot be undone."[47] But what prophet declared Barnabas' doctrine, that since God has shown mercy on the Gentiles, He will not show them the great things of His law?[48] Did Moses say that, or any of the prophets?

Uzziel, Hillel, Levi, Hilkiah, Eli, Hushai, Lamech, Benjamin, Micah, Maschil, Nadab: *No. Not one! Etc.*

Hananiah: Lastly, brothers, Barnabas was mistaken when he said it was because the elders in Antioch were "inexpert in the scriptures" that they could not confute us. Rather, they could not confute us because the truth cannot be confuted, however appealing the arguments that are raised against it.

And I will conclude with this. The promises of God regarding the heathen are as clear as they are immutable, namely, that if they obey His law, then they will be blessed along with us, His chosen people. Otherwise, they will be damned with the rest of the heathen. It is wrong to accuse us of demanding too much of the Gentiles when we demand only what God Himself has commanded all men to do – indeed, when we demand only what Messiah Jesus taught and whose example of keeping the law, I remind you, we were all following when God set His seal of approval upon us and our faith by pouring out His Spirit on us! [*Hananiah sits.*]

Council members: *Comments.*

Silas: It is easy to see why the elders in Antioch found it difficult to determine the truth in this matter.

---

[46] Isa. 56:6–7.

[47] Jn. 10:35.

[48] Cf. Hos. 8:12.

Council members: *Comments.*

A Flaw in Hananiah's Doctrine Is Corrected

Nahum: Men and brothers, Hananiah has presented arguments which must be addressed, for many of our people who believe will think the same thoughts and need clear answers. First, the prophets did indeed speak of the Gentiles coming to Israel and joining our nation in order to serve God. That cannot be denied. Second, God did set His seal of approval upon the faith of us who were keeping the law when He sealed us with His Spirit, and He has continued for many years now to bless those in Israel who do the same. So, Barnabas, my son, what do you say to those truths?

Barnabas: As for the first point, Nahum, we know that the Gentiles will someday join with Israel to serve the Lord; the prophets spoke plainly of that day. But a careful reading of those prophecies shows that they refer to the Gentiles coming to Israel to serve God *after* Messiah returns, not now, for it is written, "I will return, and I will dwell in the midst of Jerusalem,"[49] and "all nations whom you have made will come and bow down before you, O Lord, and they will glorify your name."[50] But the Gentiles cannot come to Jerusalem and bow down before the Lord Jesus if he is not here, can they?

Council members: *Comments.*

Barnabas: Therefore, Jesus must return before those prophecies – any of them – can be fulfilled.

Council members: *Comments.*

Hananiah: But Barnabas, you and Paul are teaching that until Jesus returns, the Gentiles are free not to submit to our law. What sense does that make? Since the day God gave the law, any Gentile who would serve God truly has been required to come serve Him as we do, and they will be required to do so after the Lord returns; so, what is the point in not requiring them to submit to His law during this brief absence of Jesus?

Council members: *Comments.*

Hananiah: If Jesus returns today and finds you teaching his believing Gentiles not to obey the law that God commands them to obey, what will you and Paul say to him?

Council members: *Comments.*

---

[49] Zech. 8:3a.

[50] Ps. 86:9.

Barnabas: Your question brings up several issues, Hananiah, but let me start with your expectation of the Lord's soon return. And I will ask this of you all. Can anyone here tell me when the Lord will return to Jerusalem so that the nations *can* come bow down to him and hear the law from his mouth?

Council members: *Comments.*

Simon Peter: The prophets did not say when those prophecies would be fulfilled because they did not know. They prophesied both of Jesus' sufferings and of his glory, but they did not understand what the Spirit was saying through them. God told them only that their prophecies were not for their own time.

Council members: *Comments.*

Barnabas: Hananiah, what do *you* say? When will the prophecies you mentioned come to pass?

Hananiah: Peter is right. We do not know precisely, but soon, surely.

Barnabas: How soon?

Hananiah: As soon as Jesus returns. And that will certainly be soon, for what would be the point of delaying the fulfillment of prophecies he has begun to fulfill? He has fulfilled the gruesome part, his great suffering and death. Nothing awaits now but his glory.

Jared: The angels that appeared to us at Bethany as we watched Jesus ascend into heaven said he would return, just as we saw him leave.

Barnabas: But did those angels tell you when that will happen, Jared?

Jared: Well, not specifically, no.

John: No one knows when Jesus will return. Jesus said that not even he knew, but only the Father.[51]

Council members: *Comments.*

Andrew: One evening before Jesus died, John and I sat with him on the Mount of Olives, along with John's brother, Jacobus, and Simon. We asked him about his return and the end of this age, and Jesus told us many signs to look for, which have not yet taken place and which will take years to transpire.[52]

John: And we have not yet seen any of those signs of his coming or of the end of the world.

Simon Peter: No, we have not.

Andrew: One sign which struck me is that he said Jerusalem would be destroyed before he comes back to us.

Council members: *Comments.*

---

[51] Mk. 13:32.

[52] Mt. 24; Mk. 13; Lk. 21.

Barnabas: Obviously then, many things must take place before Jesus returns, including the destruction and rebuilding of this city, and so, those prophecies of Gentiles coming to Jerusalem to serve Messiah must apply to the time *after* Jesus returns, not to our time.

Council members: *Comments.*

Barnabas: Also, brothers, you know that according to the prophets, every Jew that is alive in this land when Messiah Jesus returns will receive him as King, for Messiah spoke through the prophet Zechariah and said he would "pour out on the house of David and on the inhabitant of Jerusalem the spirit of grace and of supplication, and they will look to me whom they pierced."[53] And on that day, all Israel "will mourn for him as one mourns for an only son, bitterly crying out for him as one would bitterly cry out for a firstborn. The wailing in Jerusalem that day will be great."[54] That generation of our people will be "an afflicted and lowly people,"[55] but God chose them before the world began, to be humbled by great suffering and receive Messiah when he returns, for the angel told Daniel, "At that time, your people will be delivered, every one who is found written in the Book."[56] And the prophet Zechariah said that if in those days, any Jew refuses to submit to Messiah, even his own parents will have a hand in killing him![57]

Council members: *Comments.*

Barnabas: Now, look around you, in this city and beyond. You know how it is. Do you think every soul in this perverse generation that cursed Jesus and that persecutes us who believe would bow at Jesus' feet and receive him if God were to send him back today?

Council members: *No. Not at all. Etc.*

Barnabas: Or would our wicked rulers kill a man for *not* believing in Jesus? On the contrary, they would bless him.

Council members: *That is true. Yes, they would. Etc.*

Barnabas: God is ready to avenge all disobedience, but Israel's obedience must be fulfilled first, and though God has brought many thousands in Israel into this grace, there are many more thousands who reject Jesus, including most of our rulers and judges.

Council members: *Amen. That is true. Etc.*

---

[53] Zech. 12:10a.

[54] Zech. 12:10b–11a.

[55] Zeph. 3:12b.

[56] Dan. 12:1b.

[57] Zech. 13:3.

Barnabas: No, brothers, God will not send His Son to Israel again or bring the Gentiles to bow at his feet until He has utterly crushed and humbled this stiff-necked people, for the prophets said, "I will bring distress upon Jerusalem, and there will be mourning and moaning. And when you are abased, you will speak from the ground, and your talk will be humbled in the dirt,"[58] "and they shall know that I, the LORD, did not say in vain that I would bring this evil upon them."[59]

Philip: And because he knew that would happen, Jesus wept over Jerusalem and said, "O Jerusalem! Jerusalem, who kills the prophets and stones those who are sent to her! Behold! *Your* house is left to *you*, desolate. I tell *you* that *you* will by no means see me until the time comes when *you* say, 'Blessed is he who comes in the name of the LORD.'"[60]

Hananiah: But I was with you when Jesus said that, Philip. He was in a village on his way to Jerusalem for the last time.[61] And when he arrived and was riding that donkey into the city, the multitude did rejoice greatly and cry out, "Blessed is he who comes in the name of the LORD!"[62] His prophecy *was* fulfilled. Do you remember?

Philip: Yes, they did that, and I remember thinking then, as you obviously did, how amazing it was that Jesus had told us beforehand that the people would cry out like that when he came. And seeing that, we all felt doubly certain that Jesus was about to set up his kingdom.

Matthew: The people thought so, too, and began crying out, "Blessed is the coming kingdom of our father David,"[63] and "Blessed is the King of Israel who is coming in the name of the LORD!"[64]

Philip: We were all excited, expecting Jesus to set up his kingdom right away.

Council members: *Comments.*

Philip: But here is something you do not know, Hananiah, because you were not with us a few days later when Jesus was in the temple, teaching. I was surprised, and I think we all were, to see that Jesus was still grieving for Jerusalem and to hear him say, even more passionately

---

[58] Isa. 29:2a, 4a.

[59] Ezek. 6:10.

[60] Lk. 13:34a, 35.

[61] Cf. Lk. 13:22.

[62] Mt. 21:9; Mk. 11:9.

[63] Mk. 11:10.

[64] Lk. 19:38; Jn. 12:13.

than before, that the city would not see him again until they welcomed him.[65]

Hananiah: [*thoughtfully*] I didn't know he said it again, after he came into the city.

Silas: It's true, Hananiah. I was there in the temple when he said it.

Hananiah: So, when he made that statement on the way here, he was talking about his Second Coming, and not his triumphant entrance into Jerusalem?

Philip: It must be so. Otherwise, why would he have still been grieving days later, after he was here in the city?

Barnabas: God will certainly send His Son again from heaven to rescue Israel, Hananiah, but that day will not come until this nation has been thoroughly chastened and humbled. Then, the whole nation will cry out together, "Blessed is he who comes in the name of the LORD!"

Hananiah: I do see what you are saying.

Matthew: We were wrong, all of us, about these things in the beginning, Hananiah. And we continued to be wrong even after Jesus ascended into heaven, for we still expected him to return quickly to establish his kingdom.

John: I certainly did.

Jacobus: I believed the same thing.[66]

Simon Peter: I even declared that the time was at hand for the moon to turn to blood and the sun to turn black.[67]

Andrew: It seemed plausible at first, but in retrospect, we should have known that Jesus was not coming back any time soon. None of the things he had told us to look for had happened.

Simon Peter: Yes. Odd, isn't it, how we can know things, and yet, not know them?

Philip: It certainly is.

Azariah: We had plenty of good reasons to think the wrong thing.

Elkanah: Good ideas are like knives, the better they are, the worse they can hurt you.

Council members: [*Laughing*] *That's the truth. Amen, Elkanah. Etc.*

Azariah: And our particular good idea was that since the prophets spoke of Messiah coming to us like the early and latter rains,[68] the two rainy seasons God has given this land was a sign that Messiah would give

---

65 Mt. 23:37–39.

66 As is seen in James 5:8–9.

67 Acts 2:16–21.

68 Hos. 6:3; Joel 2:23.

us his two outpourings of the Spirit within a year, the early rain being the outpouring on the Pentecost right after Jesus ascended, and the latter rain being the outpouring Jesus will bring to Israel when he returns.

Ahijah: Yes. So, it seemed reasonable to assume that the "former rain and latter rain" of the Spirit would come within that first year.

Micah: Do you no longer believe Jesus will do that when he returns?

Ahijah: Oh, yes. We know that when Jesus returns, he will pour out the Spirit a second time, for the prophets said, "On that day, there will be a fountain opened for the house of David and the inhabitants of Jerusalem for sin and uncleanness,"[69] "and I will forgive their blood-guiltiness which I had not forgiven."[70] But, obviously, the latter rain did not fall on Israel within a year of the first one.

Maschil: But might not that latter rain yet take place soon? More than two decades have passed since Messiah ascended into heaven, and we certainly do not expect him to wait a hundred more.

Simon Peter: A thousand years is like one day to God, Maschil. Moses even said that a thousand years is to God "like yesterday when it is past, or like a watch in the night."[71] We just do not know what God has planned, or if He had a plan and changed it.

Council members: *Amen. He may have. Etc.*

Andrew: Our God is not just a bigger one of us, as the heathen view their gods, sharing our perspective of time. Messiah's former and latter rains may be very far apart, Maschil, from our perspective. We just don't know.

Council members: *Comments.*

Andrew: When Jesus was here with us, we misunderstood so much! I remember that after he rose from the dead, when he suddenly appeared in our hiding place, he told us that he was sending us to preach, just as the Father had sent him, and when he breathed out toward us and said, "Receive the Spirit,"[72] I thought that he meant he was giving us the Spirit right then.

Bartholomew: So did I. I thought he was giving us the Spirit then and there and that we should go out and start preaching.

Simon Peter: I did, too. But that was because none of us knew what receiving the Spirit meant.

---

[69] Zech. 13:1.

[70] Joel 3:21a.

[71] Ps. 90:4. The only Psalm attributed to Moses.

[72] Jn. 20:19–22.

Bartholomew: Right. But it sounded as if Jesus was talking about something taking place at that moment.

Philip: Yes, it did. But we were not sent, and he did not give us the Spirit until Pentecost.

Apostles: *Amen. That's right. Etc.*

Barnabas: Even later, I was so sure that Jesus was returning soon that I sold all my possessions and brought the proceeds here to lay at your feet. What need did I have of houses and lands if I was about to reign with Jesus over the whole world?

Council members: *Comments.*

Barnabas: But time passed, and we were forced to admit that it was not as we had thought.

Simon Peter: That is true, Barnabas.

Council members: *Comments.*

Joseph: Do you see that, Hananiah?

Hananiah: Yes. I already knew that many Gentiles would join with Israel to serve Messiah after he returns, but I do see now that Jesus will not return as soon as some of us have thought. On that point, I admit that I was mistaken.

Daniel: There is no disgrace in being wrong, Hananiah. The disgrace is in refusing to be made right.

Council members: *Comments.*

Hananiah: I may have hurt my own argument by misapplying those particular scriptures, and I regret that because what I am trying to communicate is true. Still, I am thankful for the insight you have given me. I am always grateful for a more perfect understanding of the ways of our God.

Daniel: Solomon defined a wise man as one who can still learn, Hananiah.[73] You have shown that you are wise, in that you can still be instructed.

Hananiah: I am not ashamed to be made wiser, Daniel. The truth concerning Messiah Jesus is all I want, and only that will I embrace if God gives me the grace to hear His wisdom.

Council members: *Amen! God help us! Etc.*

Nahum: This is good, brothers. May God continue to grant us peace.

Council members: *Amen! God help us! Etc.*

---

[73] Prov. 1:5.

Hananiah Adds to His Argument

Nahum: But let us now put aside the matter of when Jesus will return, since no one knows when that will be. God may not send Jesus back even in the lifetime of the youngest man here. Whether sooner or later, however, the issue is whether or not we are to command believing Gentiles to keep our law now.

This must be addressed, brothers, not only to bring rest to the Assembly in Antioch, but also to ensure peace in the household of God in every place, for the matter touches upon the very nature of this new covenant which God has made with us. Barnabas and Paul testify that Messiah has given them a gospel for the Gentiles which does not require that they keep the law. Then, what shall we say of the gospel Jesus preached, which *does* require men to keep the law, and which gospel we still preach?

Silas: Yes, it is beyond dispute, as Hananiah said, that God set His seal upon our gospel by granting us His Spirit, and it is beyond dispute that God is continuing to do so in Israel. What Hananiah disputes is Barnabas' contention that beginning with Cornelius, God also set His seal on a different gospel.

Hananiah: Yes, that is it, Silas. But before Barnabas answers, I would like to add something.

Silas: Of course.

Hananiah: [*Hananiah rises again.*] Brothers, I have already explained that God's mercy and patience with the ignorant does not mean that He excuses transgression when it is self-willed, but that He expects better of ignorant souls after they have obtained mercy. What Barnabas and Paul see as God setting His seal upon a different gospel, I see as God showing mercy to ignorant souls, but expecting them to learn to do His will or be condemned, as the law teaches, and as we were teaching the Gentiles in Antioch before we were interrupted.

It remains clear to me – and in this, I think I will not be proved wrong – that God's will for all men is, and always will be, that they honor His law as well as His Son. That is the gospel with which we began, and it is our sacred duty to proclaim it, for it has been confirmed by the Spirit of God.

Council members: *Comments.*

Hananiah: God foretold this gospel through Isaiah, saying, "To the law and to the testimony! If they do not speak according to this word, it is because there is no light in them."[74] We agree with God, brothers, that there is no light in men who "do not speak according to this word"! It was, in fact, to enable us to refute challenges to our gospel that God so clearly defined the right path. He knew that challenges such as this new gospel would come, and so, He defined the true gospel so plainly that even the simplest man can understand it. The path of righteousness is the path of the law *and* the testimony of Jesus, the Spirit of God.[75] The law testified beforehand that the Son was coming, and the Spirit testifies now that he came and that he is coming again. The law and the Spirit work together to bring glory to God, and it is by adhering to those two immutable gifts from God that we please God and gain sufficient wisdom to judge between the true doctrine and the vain doctrines devised by men.

I thank God that we are not left to ourselves to decide upon the right way. I thank God that He sent the Spirit to be that gentle voice behind us, whispering, "This is the way; walk in it!"[76] And the "it" which the voice of God is telling us to walk in is the way Jesus walked, brothers, the way Isaiah foretold: "To the law and to the testimony!"

Council members: *Comments.*

Hananiah: God's law and God's Spirit are both in my heart, brothers. I am compelled by the love of God to preach them both, together. I must proclaim what I hear whispered in my ear, and what I hear is the gospel which our Lord Jesus preached and commanded us to preach.[77] I must proclaim, "To the law and to the testimony! This is the way; walk in it!" And if I am wrong in walking by that light, may God have mercy on my soul. I can do nothing else. How can it be any other way? [*Hananiah sits.*]

Council members: *Comments.*

Daniel: Brother Hananiah, you have communicated your position in a manner that commends both you and it. Barnabas and Paul will tell you that your argument is weak, as you must expect, but I hasten to add that I see no weakness in your spirit. Plain speech comes from a pure heart and is easily understood, and it is always welcome among the upright. Contentiousness in any cause is ungodly, and a wise servant of God never demeans the faith by quarreling over it, though he may speak forcefully in its defense, as you have attempted to do. So, I commend you, brother, for balancing a godly attitude with straightforward speech.

---

[74] Isa. 8:20.

[75] Jn. 15:26. See also 1John 5:6 and Revelation 19:10.

[76] Isa. 30:21.

[77] Lk. 12:3.

Council members: *Comments.*

Daniel: That said, let me encourage you to hear these men patiently, for they seek to perfect your faith. Incomplete truth can wield complete control over the soul, but the purging of the heart from imperfect thoughts yields perfect peace.

Council members: *Comments.*

Nahum: Barnabas and Paul, you know that from the time of Moses until now, God has required the heathen to be circumcised if they would be a part of His covenant with Israel, and to submit to our law if they would serve Him truly.

Barnabas: Yes, of course.

Paul: Yes.

Nahum: Then, respond now to Hananiah's second point, for you men teach that God no longer requires the heathen to receive circumcision or to keep our law.

Joseph: Brother Paul, we would hear from you, son.

Paul: Sir, I am content for Barnabas to continue.

Joseph: Nevertheless, we would hear what you have to say.

Barnabas: Go ahead, Paul.

Nahum: Yes, son. Barnabas is free to add what he will after you have spoken.

PART 2
PAUL EXPLAINS AND DEFENDS HIS GOSPEL

—❦—

Paul Explains the Foundation of His Gospel

Paul: Very well, I will do as you ask. [*Paul rises.*] Men and brothers, it is fitting that you who govern in the house of God should demand that Barnabas and I give an account of our ministry. And we gladly do so, for in speaking to the Gentiles about Messiah Jesus, we represent not only him, but also you and God's saints everywhere. And aware of that, I assure you, we conduct ourselves in all purity and sincerity among them.

Council members: *Comments.*

Paul: It is not for lack of eagerness to answer that I have remained silent, but I felt compelled to wait for my elders and to hear first from those who were in the faith before me.

Jacobus: Speak freely Paul. You are among brothers here.

Council members: *Comments.*

Paul: Thank you, Jacobus. I will. Men and brothers, what I say, I say as a servant of God who should give account of himself to his betters. Yet, I do not speak so as to please you any more than I speak to the Gentiles to please them. To all men and in all places, I say only what Messiah has taught me to say. And the gospel he has sent me to preach, I preach without respect of persons and with great plainness of speech. Therefore, I pray that you will receive kindly my direct manner.

Council members: *Comments.*

Paul: First of all, brothers, I would have you to know that in whatever foreign city Barnabas and I find our Jewish kinsman, we do exactly as Hananiah has said. We preach Jesus to them and encourage them to continue in the law of our fathers. In other words, we tell them, "To the law and to the Spirit." You may have heard the slander about Barnabas and me, that we teach Jews to forsake Moses.[78] That is false. We have never attempted to persuade any of our nation to cease worshipping according to the customs Moses passed down to us.

Council members: *Comments.*

Paul: Moreover, in no village or city do we preach to the uncircumcised before presenting ourselves to the Jews of that place, if any are

---

[78] Acts 21:21.

there. For the gospel must be preached first to the Jews, and only then to the Gentiles.

Council members: *Comments.*

Nahum: We would expect no less of you and Barnabas, Paul. That is good and right. But how do you answer Hananiah?

Paul: My answer to Hananiah will be hard for some to hear; so, if you will allow me, I would lay some groundwork for it.

Joseph: No one will be troubled by that, brother Paul. We have come together to hear you.

Nahum: Yes, go ahead, son.

Paul: Men and brothers, in preparation for this meeting, I have been pondering this question: What is the foundation of the gospel that Jesus has given me? And after much contemplation, I have concluded that the foundation of my gospel is the unique authority of Messiah Jesus to save. He is the one whom the prophet said God would make "most blessed, forever,"[79] for God has exalted Jesus above all things and placed all power in his hand; nothing can be added to him, and nothing can be taken away. Jesus has all power to save forever those who come to God by him, and nothing but Jesus can save at all. He needs nothing, and all that we need is in him. He is uniquely our Savior, and from that truth springs all else that I know and teach.

Council members: *Comments.*

Paul: God is holier and higher than the heavens, brothers. He abases Himself even to look upon what is in heaven, much less to view the wickedness of earth.[80] As Job said, "Even the heavens are not clean in His sight."[81] There, into the highest heaven, God has exalted Jesus to reign in glory at His right hand, far above everything that has a name or that can be named, and all glory that is glory is now his.

This unique glory of the Son of God is the rock upon which my gospel rests. Compared to his glory, the glory of the prophets fades away, for the only glory they had was the glory they received from God to prophesy of things about which they knew nothing, especially His hidden Son. But the Son has now been revealed and has redeemed us, and in him alone should we glory if we glory at all.

John: That is so good, Paul. Amen!

Council members: *Comments.*

---

[79] Ps. 21:6.

[80] Ps. 113:6.

[81] Job 15:15b; cf. Job 4:18b.

Paul Argues that Men Have a Sinful Nature

Paul: Brothers, even those who obeyed the law perfectly needed a Redeemer, did they not? But from what did Messiah redeem them if they were made perfect by the law? I myself was blameless according to the law when I persecuted God's saints. But what was so powerful and malevolent that even the law of Moses did not deliver us? What was so powerful and malevolent that we could not resist it, except God's Son die and provide us the power of His Spirit? I will tell you what we could not conquer – the corrupt nature that is in our own flesh! We could not escape our carnal nature! And being unable to deliver us from the dominion of our corrupt nature, the law could only act as the warden of the prison in which we dwelt.

Hushai: The warden of our prison? God's law, *a warden*? The law taught us the ways of God, Paul. That is the way of a father, not a warden!

Council members: *Comments.*

Hushai: David said, "I will live in liberty, for I delight in your commandments and meditate on your statutes."[82] David was liberated by the law, not imprisoned by it! David loved God's commandments more than fine gold,[83] and God's law was his great delight.[84] Does that sound like a man who saw the law as a warden?

Council members: *Comments.*

Hushai: And if David was liberated by the law, why is it, Paul, that you feel so bound by it that you see it as your warden? Could it be that you have a secret desire to be like the Gentiles, which makes you feel imprisoned by the law that commands you not to be like them?

Paul: I have no desire to be like either the Gentiles or the Jews. My only desire is to be like Jesus. But to make it clear, I do not teach, and I did not say that *the law* was our prison. Our prison is the carnal nature we inherited from Adam, and the law was indeed the warden of it, for until Messiah came, we all were held in custody under the law, which restrained our fleshly nature.

Council members: *Comments.*

Paul: Messiah did indeed speak through David about loving the law, Hushai, but he was referring to the law that I preach, the law of the Spirit. Messiah loves that law more than he loves the law of Moses.

---

[82] Ps. 119:44–48.

[83] Ps. 119:127.

[84] Ps. 119:77, 174.

Hushai: You speak as if God's law is not Moses' law, but God said many times that Moses' law *was* His![85]

Paul: Yes, but God gave that law to Moses, for He had another law hidden in His Son – the eternal law of the Spirit.

Council members: *Comments.*

Hushai: God did not give the law away like some worn-out tool! He gave it for us to keep!

Paul: . . . but only until Messiah brought us the law of the Spirit of life, the law which God now commands all men to obey, and by which He Himself lives.

Council members: *Comments.*

Benjamin: I am confused. What are you saying, brother Paul?

Paul: Under the law, Benjamin, everything was in the flesh – the feasts, the sacrifices, even the wars that Israel fought – all were in the flesh. But in this covenant, everything is in the Spirit. Our souls feast on manna from heaven, we offer sacrifices of praise from sanctified hearts, and we wage war against the invisible powers of this age, not against flesh and blood.

Lamech: God's way is not an either/or thing, Paul. God does not call on us to choose between the law and the Spirit; He commands both, just as Hananiah said, and just as Jesus showed us while he was here. Jesus never taught such things as you teach, including what you are saying about a sinful nature. He came to redeem Israel from her enemies, not from herself.

Andrew: Jesus tried to tell us when he was here, Lamech, that God was about to change the standard from Moses' law to the law of the Spirit. Do any of you remember Jesus' sermon on the mountain, when he kept saying, "You have heard it said . . . but I say. . ."?

Apostles who had been with Jesus, and Hananiah and Micah: *Yes, we do. Amen. Etc.*

Andrew: You were there, Lamech. Do you remember that?

Lamech: Yes, I remember.

Andrew: Over and over again, the Lord quoted Moses and then told us of a new standard by which men would be judged. Moses commanded men not to murder, but Jesus said that now, if a man hates his brother without cause, he is guilty of murder, even if he does not commit the act.[86] And Moses commanded men not to commit adultery, but Jesus said that now, God will judge a man to be guilty of adultery if he merely lusts for a

---

[85] Ex. 16:4; 2Chron. 6:16, et. al.

[86] Mt. 5:21–22.

woman.[87] We didn't understand him at the time, but he was laboring to prepare us for this great change, which we could not then even imagine.

Simon Peter: And do you remember the time we asked Jesus who could be saved, and he said, "With men, it is impossible"?

Apostles who had been with Jesus: *Yes, he did. Etc.*

Simon Peter: We were speechless. What were we to do, if we could do nothing to be saved? But he was only telling us that with *our* kind of life, we can never measure up to the standard that God was about to require. We needed the power of God's life, the Spirit, within us.

Paul: Yes. In this covenant, a man without the Spirit *cannot* do the will of God, but when we walk in His Spirit, we do His will without even thinking about it, for it becomes our nature to do it.

John: God's commandments are not burdensome to the man who walks in the Spirit because they are no longer foreign to his nature.

Simon Peter: . . . because by the Spirit, we have become partakers of God's holy nature.

Paul: Exactly. A man without God's Spirit is, as I say it, living "in the flesh", and such a man cannot please God because it is impossible for anyone "in the flesh" to obey the law of the Spirit. Anybody in the flesh can practice Moses' law, even the wicked. And they have often done so.

Council members: *Comments.*

Paul: And as for Israel's need of a Redeemer from a sinful nature, the Spirit said through David, "There is no one doing good. The LORD looked down from heaven upon the sons of man to see if there was anyone with understanding, anyone who was seeking God. They have all turned aside. They are all, alike, corrupted; there is no one doing good, not even one!"[88]

Hushai: But God was speaking only of those in Israel who had turned away from the law, Paul. Did you not hear what David said: "They have all *turned aside*"?

Paul: Then what did Isaiah mean when he said *of Israel*, "We all, like sheep, have gone astray; every one of us has turned to his own way," and of the Messiah, "the LORD has laid upon him the iniquity of us all"?[89] Or what did David mean when he begged God, "No one living is righteous before you."[90] No, Hushai, God was not speaking of Israel's turning away from the law, but of mankind's turning away *from Him*. And that truth leads us to another one, namely, if we were still in bondage to sin after the

---

[87] Mt. 5:27–28.

[88] Ps. 14:1b–3.

[89] Isa. 53:6.

[90] Ps. 143:2.

law was given, then the law did not cure the sinfulness of men who kept it.

Council members: *Comments.*

Paul: Therefore, we conclude that all men, whether keeping the law or not, come short of the righteousness of God, and all are in bondage to sin until Jesus redeems their soul from it by the power of the Spirit. That is the very reason the Spirit moved David to plead with God, "Fulfill your law from within!"[91]

Council members: *Comments.*

Jared: And this is the revelation that you have received, that all men have a sinful nature, and the law can do nothing about it?

Paul: In part, yes. The law cannot *change* man's nature; it can only *restrain* it with threats of punishment by the judges. But in this covenant, the Spirit makes us a new kind of men – creatures with a fleshly body but with God's nature within it. This creation has never seen such creatures as we are in Messiah Jesus. And of all creatures in every realm, this new creature alone is able to please God and serve Him the way He must be served.

Hushai: Jesus possessed God's eternal Spirit while he was here, Paul, and he served God well – under the law!

Council members: *Comments.*

Hushai: *He* is the example that we follow, and believers everywhere were happily following his example before you began preaching your gospel; then, men began following you, instead.

Paul: I want no man to follow me except as I follow Jesus.

Hushai: Then, follow Jesus, and we will all follow you!

Uzziel, Hillel, Levi, Hilkiah, Eli, Lamech, Benjamin, Micah, Maschil, Nadab: *Yes! That's right. Etc.*

Hushai: Brothers, look to Moses and the prophets, not to Paul and Barnabas! Moses and the prophets spoke of redemption hundreds of times, but never – not once! – did they speak of redemption from a sinful nature. This gospel Paul proclaims is no gospel at all; it is heathen philosophical blather. The Gentiles love such vain talk, but it has no place among the righteous.

The redemption of Israel is a lasting deliverance from oppression by foreign powers. That is our hope, and that is God's promise. He re-deemed us out of bondage in Egypt[92] in order to give us His law; He re-

---

[91] Ps. 74:11.

[92] Dt. 7:8.

deemed us out of captivity in Babylon,[93] that we might dwell again in this land and keep the law; and He has now raised up Jesus to redeem us again from the heathen that oppress us – and He will return and do so if we keep His law! Isaiah said, "If *you* be willing and obedient, *you* shall eat the good of the land, but if *you* refuse and *you* are rebellious, *you* will be consumed by the sword."[94] And these things, all the prophets say!

Uzziel, Hillel, Levi, Hilkiah, Eli, Lamech, Benjamin, Micah, Maschil, Nadab: *Amen! That's right. Etc.*

Lamech: Brothers, do not allow Paul's poison into this Assembly! It has infected the Assembly in Antioch already, and we were ministering to them the healing balm of truth when these men stopped us.

John: Brothers, be careful. Jesus once angered some who believed in him by saying, "If *you* abide in my word, *you* are truly my disciples, and *you* shall know the truth, and the truth shall make *you* free."

Benjamin: How could that have angered anyone, brother John?

John: It angered them, Benjamin, because they were thinking carnally, the way Hushai and Lamech are thinking now. And thinking of bodily slavery, they responded to Jesus, "We have never been slaves to any man. How can you say, '*You* shall be free'?" Then Jesus explained to them the truth he was trying to convey: "Everyone who commits sin is a slave of sin."[95] But it was useless; they would not hear it. In fact, they were so angry with Jesus that they called him a bastard, suggesting that Mary had been impregnated by a Samaritan, and then they said he was demon-possessed.[96]

Daniel: Pride is a crafty foe, Benjamin, especially when it uses truth to justify itself. There is no pride like the pride of those who are right in what they know, but do not know the mind of God. There is no hatred like religious hatred, for when a man believes that God approves of his hatred, he thinks that to show love or mercy is sinful. To such a man, cruelty toward the ungodly is a righteous act.

When Jesus returned to Nazareth after his Temptation, he angered almost everybody in our synagogue by declaring God's love for the Gentiles. The men of the synagogue rose up in anger and dragged him out of the city, and they would have thrown Jesus from the rocks and killed him except that God made a way for him to escape.[97] Those men knew

---

[93] Isa. 48:20; Jer. 50:34; Mic. 4:10.

[94] Isa. 1:19–20.

[95] Jn. 8:31–34.

[96] Jn. 8:48.

[97] Lk. 4:16–30.

that they were God's chosen people, but being ignorant of God's heart toward others, they were hard-hearted against Gentiles, puffed up by the little truth they knew.

So, brother Hushai, yes, it is true that God redeemed our fathers from slavery in Egypt, and then from captivity in Babylon, and it is also true that Jesus will return and subdue the nations and exalt Israel above them all. But the truth to which your pride blinds you is that Jesus will return and reign over the earth from Jerusalem only after the stubborn pride of this nation is crushed, just as Barnabas said earlier. And God will certainly do it. Beware that you are not crushed with it. Do you understand this, Hushai?

Hushai: Yes, but understanding it and agreeing with it are not the same thing, Daniel.

Andrew: Hushai, I beg you to consider carefully what you are being told.

Hushai: Do you think I have not been considering these things? Since Barnabas and Paul confronted us in Antioch, that is all that I have considered.

Council members: *Comments.*

Andrew: Hushai, a man approached us one day as Jesus passed by a certain place and told him that he would follow him but that first, he needed to go home to bury his father. Jesus said to him, "You follow me, and leave the dead to bury their dead!"[98] That sounded so strange to us! How could the dead bury the dead? And Jesus said similar things in those days which also puzzled us, but you see, he was walking in a kind of life which enabled him to see things differently, things to which we were truly "dead", to use his term.

Hushai: Who doesn't agree that Jesus knew more than we do, Andrew?

Andrew: But it is not just that Jesus knew more than we did. He saw things and understood things that no man can see and understand without the kind of life he possessed. We were not just sleeping or fuzzy-headed concerning the things of God; we were altogether dead to them, as are all men without the Spirit. We did not see ourselves as dead, of course, but we *were* dead to the things of God, and Jesus knew it. And he also knew he had been sent by God to wake us from the dead, as the prophet said, "Arise! Shine! For your light has come, and the glory of the Lord has risen upon you!"[99] And now, being born of the Spirit, we are children of

---

[98] Mt. 8:21–22; cf. Lk. 9:60.

[99] Isa. 60:1.

the light, and we should rejoice in that light of God, not in the darkness that used to cover us.

Hushai: Such speeches may sound weighty to some, Andrew, but isn't it remarkable that, by one way or another, they all eventually lead to calling God's law darkness? Clever speeches attract only those who are not fully committed to the law of God.

Micah: The law of God is our glory, Andrew, our testimony to all the nations of God's love for Israel. Moses told Israel that keeping the law "will be *your* wisdom and *your* understanding in the eyes of the nations, and they will say, 'Truly, this great nation is a wise and understanding people!'"[100] The law of our God is a light to the whole world, and Israel was chosen by God to carry it.

The True Light

John: Yes, Micah, but the true light came from heaven and dwelt among us,[101] and that is far better.

Micah: I know that the light Jesus brought is better, John, but did not the law also come from heaven? David did not call the law darkness; he said, "The commandment is a lamp, and the law is light."[102]

Barnabas: The light of the law is the Lord himself, Micah. The law is but a pale reflection of him. The law has no light of its own; it is like shimmering water, reflecting the light of the sun, but when the sun is hidden, the water is dark.

Hananiah: Those who walk in the light of God's law never walk in darkness, Barnabas.

Cleopas: The law was only a reflection of the light which God was hiding, Hananiah. Jesus said that he, not the law, is the light of the world.[103] And it most certainly came from God, Micah, who alone knew that He was hiding a Son.

Micah: What Jesus actually said, Cleopas, is that he was the light of the world *as long as he was in the world*.[104] But he is no longer here, which means that *we* are now God's lights in this world, as Jesus also said.[105] Jesus shined most brightly, to be sure, but God has never left Himself with but one light. The law was shining in the world when David

---

[100] Dt. 4:5–6.

[101] Jn. 1:7–9, 14.

[102] Prov. 6:23.

[103] Jn. 8:12.

[104] Jn. 9:5.

[105] Mt. 5:14.

said, "The heavens declare the glory of God, and the firmament displays the work of His hands."[106]   So, the law and nature were both lights, working together at the same time to lead men to God.

Maschil: And the prophets, too. Were they not shining along with the law?

Matthew: They were all just reflections of the mighty Son of God, and compared to his glory, they were all darkness.

Council members: *Comments.*

Matthew: Let me ask you, Maschil, to whom did God send Messiah Jesus?

Maschil: God sent him, and the prophets, and His law, to Israel, His chosen people.

Matthew: Yes. Then, was not the prophet referring to Israel when he spoke of Messiah and said, "The people who walk in darkness have seen a great light, and on those who dwell in the land of the shadow of death, light has shined"?[107]

Maschil: [*thoughtfully*]. I suppose so, yes. I can see that.

Micah: Every man here can see that, Matthew, but you and others are taking true things and stretching them beyond their ordained limits.

Matthew: I think not, Micah. Messiah alone brought us the life that enlightens man's eyes and delivers him from darkness.

The True Righteousness and Knowledge of God

Paul: That is what Jesus taught me, Matthew. When we enter into God's kind of life – or rather, when it enters into us – all things become new to us, for God said, "My thoughts are not your thoughts, and my ways are not your ways."[108]

Micah: Who does not agree with that, Paul? But if God's thoughts and ways are not the ones revealed in the law of Moses, then whose thoughts and ways are they? God was condemning *men's* thoughts and ways, not His own which He revealed to Moses.

Paul: Moses' law contains *some* of God's thoughts and ways, but not nearly all of them, and *reading about them* in a book is not the same as possessing God's thoughts and ways within ourselves. With God's life, we feel God's kind of love and we know how to treat others without reading it in a book; we possess God's kind of wisdom and speak truths that

---

[106] Ps. 19:1.

[107] Isa. 9:2.

[108] Isa. 55:8–9.

no law contains; and we walk in His holiness, which this earth had never witnessed until Messiah walked on earth with it.

Every man here has made decisions and done righteous deeds that were not commanded in the law. They were things given to us by the Spirit of God, things that became part of our nature when we received the Spirit. That is why I preach that with God's life alone do we have hope of salvation and by the power of that endless life, God has made Messiah Jesus our only means of salvation.

Council members: *Comments.*

John: Amen! The last night Jesus spent with us, he said he was giving us a new commandment, and then he said, "As I have loved *you*, so *you* also must love one another."[109] I thought he meant that we should love each other *better* than we had done before. But then, when the Spirit came, I experienced a love that I had never known. It was God's kind of love, the love with which Jesus had loved us. Then I understood that what he had said was just another way of telling us that we needed the Spirit, for the Spirit filled our hearts with God's kind of love and made us able to love each other the way Jesus had loved us.

Council members: *Comments.*

Paul: Moses' law did not give men the righteousness of God, brothers, for only in God's kind of life is found God's kind of righteousness, and when the Son came into the world with it, he exposed what we knew as righteousness to be no righteousness at all, as Isaiah said, "We all are like an unclean thing, and all our righteousnesses are like a filthy garment."[110] And David agreed, saying, "Every man in his best state is altogether vanity."[111] For what brought man into his "best state" but God's law, which taught men how they should live? Moreover, they were law-keeping Jews who hated Jesus and had him killed because when he came, they were exposed as unrighteous within. Man's kind of righteousness makes men proud, and proud men despise those who walk in the righteousness of God, for His righteousness exposes theirs to be vain.

Silas: This is truth which everyone will do well to consider. Moses himself said, "It will be *our* righteousness, if we are careful to do all this law."[112]

Council members: *Comments.*

---

[109] Jn. 13:34.

[110] Isa. 64:6.

[111] Ps. 39:5.

[112] Dt. 6:25.

Paul: Amen, Silas. Now, brothers, God did not condemn our fathers for their lack of His righteousness, for He had not yet revealed it, and our fathers were walking in all the righteousness God had shown them. But the fact that the law did not bring in the righteousness of God is seen in Isaiah, when God said – more than seven hundred years after the law was given – "My salvation is near to come, and my righteousness, to be revealed."[113] And Gabriel, in revealing to Daniel the precise year when Messiah would appear, said that Messiah would come and "atone for iniquity, and bring in an eternal righteousness,"[114] which he did when he purchased the Spirit for us and poured it out from heaven.

God's life is not just a higher level of our own kind of life, brothers. And God's righteousness is not just a higher level of our kind of righteousness; it is a different kind altogether. That righteousness was unknown to man before Jesus walked among us with it. And when Jesus ascended to heaven, the earth was again without that righteousness until the Spirit came and filled you with it, and now, that righteousness lives in us who believe!

Council members: *Comments.*

Paul: From the foundation of the world, God kept His Son hidden, that He might reveal him now, in our time. How blessed we are to be the generation chosen to know God's Son, for in the Son are hidden all the true knowledge and wisdom of God! No creature knew God before the Son was revealed, for no creature *can* know God unless the Son reveals God to him, as Jesus said, "No one knows the Son except the Father, nor does anyone know the Father except the Son, and he to whom the Son chooses to reveal Him."[115]

Council members: *Comments.*

Paul: Abraham was called the friend of God, but Abraham did not know his Friend. Moses, too, when he entered the sanctuary, conversed with God as a friend would speak with his friend,[116] but Moses did not know the Friend who spoke with him. David was "a man after God's own heart,"[117] but he did not know the God that his heart was like. And Daniel was "greatly loved" by God,[118] but he did not know the God who loved

---

[113] Isa. 56:1.

[114] Dan. 9:24–25.

[115] Mt. 11:27.

[116] Ex. 33:9–11.

[117] 1Sam. 13:14.

[118] Dan. 9:23.

him. All those great men of God were dead to the true knowledge of God, for the Son had not yet come and revealed that knowledge to men.

Council members: *Comments.*

Micah: Paul, forgive me, but this is difficult to hear. You are asking us to believe that men such as Noah, Daniel, and Job did not possess the knowledge of God.[119] That is so foreign to the scriptures that I can hardly believe my ears. Yes, the scriptures do say that Samuel did not know the LORD when he was a youth, but that was only because "the word of the LORD was not yet revealed to him."[120] Later, God did reveal Himself to Samuel by sending him His word.[121] That is what the scriptures say!

John: The Son of God is the Word that was not yet revealed to Samuel, or to anyone else at that time.

Micah: But the plain meaning of those scriptures, John, is that the prophet Samuel *did* come to know God after the word of God began coming to him.

Paul: The prophets and wise men knew only what God allowed them to know, Micah; the true knowledge of God was not revealed to them because God was reserving that honor for His Son.

John: If we had possessed any truth at all, Jesus would not have said that the Spirit would lead us into *all* of it.[122]

Council members: *Comments.*

Paul: The law could not give us the knowledge of God because it could not give us the Spirit, through which all true knowledge of God comes, as John just said. Before the Spirit came, it was as God told Jeremiah: "Every man is brutish in knowledge."[123] But God promised us this new covenant, by which we would receive the Spirit and obtain the knowledge of God. He said, "I will put a new spirit within them, and I will engrave my law on their heart. And they will all know me, from the least of them even to the greatest."[124]

Council members: *Comments.*

Paul: Brothers, I love the law, just as you all do. But we may now have God's kind of righteousness, and God's kind of love, and wisdom, and knowledge, and His power over sin and death. Those things are not

---

[119] Cf. Ezek. 14:14, 20.

[120] 1Sam. 3:7.

[121] 1Sam. 3:21.

[122] Jn. 16:13.

[123] Jer. 10:14a; 51:17a.

[124] Ezek. 11:19a with Jer. 31:33b, 34b.

given us by the law, but are only in the Spirit, and if the Spirit is not in us, we have none of those things, and we cannot please God.

Micah: But David said the law is perfect, Paul.[125] And that has to be true, for it is the written expression of what is in God's perfect heart.

Paul: Yes, the law is perfect, but being a handwritten document, it is limited in what it can do for us. Nothing on the outside of us can make us perfect, whether it be the law or Messiah himself. But the Spirit can enter *into us* and sanctify our souls, not just our bodies. No handwritten law can perfect us or guide us through every situation in life. There isn't enough paper or ink on earth to write down all the instructions we would need.

As perfect as the law is, even as perfect as Messiah Jesus is, both it and he are on the *outside* of man. We needed them both within us! That is why Messiah did not stay on earth when he came; if he had stayed here, he would have been just another perfect, holy thing outside of us, and our souls would have remained in bondage to sin – yes, even if he had stayed a thousand years! The Son of God came, not to stay here and reign in earthly glory, but to pay the price for us to have the perfect life of God[126] that can enter into us and make *us* perfect under a new law![127]

Council members: *Comments.*

Paul: And when Jesus rose from the dead and ascended to offer himself to God for our sins, God accepted his sacrifice and answered Jesus' prayer for us, that we, too, might have God's kind of life. And God sent it from heaven with the sound of a rushing, powerful wind, and it entered into you, Micah, and you, Hananiah, and you Hushai, and you apostles, bringing into your hearts God's law and God's testimony of His Son, and making you partakers of His very nature! Moses' law could never do that! And Jesus could never have done it if he stayed on earth.

Council members: *Comments.*

Paul: And since that first outpouring, the Spirit has been given to anyone who believes, to Barnabas and others of you here, and even to me, who once hated the name of Jesus. But God had mercy on me, and by the power of His Spirit, I was transformed, as we all were, from the ignorant creature I was into a son of the living God and brother of His Son, Jesus. That is our gospel to the Gentiles. Jesus alone can save. I do not tell them, "to the law and to the testimony", but "to Jesus", for in him alone is all of man's hope!

---

[125] Ps. 19:7.
[126] Jn. 10:10.
[127] Cf. Mt. 5:48.

Micah: We know the Spirit is wonderful, Paul, and much to be desired. And we know the awful price that was paid for us to have it. But why do you downplay the law? The law is not just another thing of man; it is the work of our God!

Paul: The *giving* of it was the work of God; the *doing* of it is the work of men.

Micah: And must not a man do what God has said?

Barnabas: Yes, of course, if God has told a man to do it. But God commanded *Israel* to keep the law; He did not command Gentiles to keep it.

Maschil: Then Israel, by keeping the law, is righteous, and the Gentiles, who do not keep the law, are not righteous!

Paul: Under the law, yes. But if our righteousness, which is by the law, had been sufficient, Maschil, Messiah would not have had to come and suffer, would he?

Council members: *Comments.*

Paul: Brothers, if there were such a thing as a law that could give men true righteousness, then righteousness would have been by Moses' law. But no handwritten law, even the perfect one God gave us, can enter a man and do that. But God's law of the Spirit can! And I praise God for it! I am not ashamed of my gospel! And I would rather praise God for His power and goodness than to debate about how powerful and good He really is!

Most Council members: *Amen! Praise God! Etc.*

Paul: Amen to God! This is my life!

Most Council members: *Amen! Praise God! Etc.*

Circumcision and the Rites of the Law

Paul: Now, brothers, it was the Son's unique honor to bring about this new and living way. No one else in heaven or earth could have done it. And now, according to the grace and foreknowledge of our God, and by faith in His sinless Son Jesus, men of any nation may obtain mercy and serve God with us, acceptably, in spirit. And upon that message, God has set His seal many times among the Gentiles, as Barnabas testified earlier.

Council members: *Comments.*

Paul: That is why Barnabas and I resisted you, Hananiah, and those with you when you came to Antioch. You were subverting the souls of those Gentiles with your gospel, telling them that putting their hope in Jesus is not enough, but that they must also be circumcised and keep the law.   Neither God nor these elders sent you to Antioch to preach the gospel of the Circumcision to uncircumcised Gentiles.

Council members: *Comments.*

Paul: I pointed out to you, before the whole Assembly in Antioch, that believing in Jesus was obviously enough for God, for He had received them into His kingdom, bearing them witness by giving them the holy Spirit just as He had given it to us. But you would not listen. You did not believe the fundamental truth of my gospel: Jesus alone saves, for only what Jesus does for a man means anything now to God.

That is what Jesus taught me. I did not learn it from man, nor even from the scriptures, but by revelation from Jesus. What I preach is his gospel, and it will withstand every contradiction. [*Paul sits.*]

Council members: *Comments.*

Hushai: The most difficult errors to expose are those which contain some truth, and there is some truth in what you men say. But our nation has always been open to foreigners who want to serve our God, as long as they serve Him the way God has commanded. Barnabas and Paul are saying the Gentiles may serve Messiah – *Israel's* Messiah! – without belonging to Israel and without following Messiah's own example of keeping the law. But God has always required the heathen to be circumcised and submit to the law if they would have their worship be acceptable to Him.

Barnabas: But God allowed uncircumcised Naaman to return uncircumcised to Syria, and He allowed him to continue to attend his king into the temple of Rimmon, as he was required to do, and even to kneel with the king as he worshipped that abomination.[128]   Naaman never kept our law; he merely loved the God who gave it. Acceptable worship is a matter of the heart, Hushai, not of proper form.

Hananiah: Of course it is, Barnabas. We all know that the law can be kept merely as a form, to maintain appearances. You and I have seen men do it, and I know that without the Spirit, men can only perform the law's rites as a form.   But to perform those rites is what God has commanded men to do. What God condemns is hypocrisy, that is, observing the form insincerely. He has never condemned the sincere observance of the form. The more secret sins a hypocrite has, the more forms he may observe, in order to cover over his great wickedness with an appearance of devotion. Who in Israel was more wicked than Caiaphas, the high priest, who performed the sacred rites of our law daily, both before he condemned Jesus

---

[128] 2Kgs. 5:17–19.

and afterward? But none of that makes useless the sincere keeping of the holy rites God has commanded.

Council members: *Comments.*

Hananiah: Once, this city became so morally wretched that God called it Sodom instead of Israel.[129] Then He went on to say that Israel had worn Him out with the multitude of their sacrifices and other observances of the law.[130] We all know that abuse of the law is evil. But the law can also be kept sincerely, with a pure heart, and that pleases God!

Council members: *Comments.*

Hananiah: It was because we in this room were keeping the law sincerely that the Almighty poured out His Spirit upon us. He has never given His Spirit to anyone in Israel who was not keeping His law from the heart, and I believe He has never given His Spirit to a Gentile without expecting that Gentile to submit to the law afterward.

Micah: Barnabas, your own experience, and ours, shows us that obedience to the law, together with faith in Jesus, pleases God, for God granted us His Spirit while we were doing both. There are many thousands of Jews who now believe, and every one of them is zealous for both the law and Messiah Jesus.[131] Doesn't that tell us something about what God requires?

Barnabas: Yes, it does, Micah. But that is *for Israel.* God has also given His Spirit to many Gentiles by the laying on of our hands, though they did not know the law. So, I return your question. Doesn't *that* tell us something about what God requires?

Maschil: The law and the prophets, with one voice, tell us repeatedly what God requires. When Jesus baptizes a man with the Spirit, that tells us only that a soul has believed in him and has done what is right in the sight of God; it does not tell us what God expects of that man afterward.

Uzziel

Uzziel: [*Uzziel rises.*] Men and brothers, I must speak.

Jacobus: Then we will listen, brother.

Nahum: What do you have to say, Uzziel?

Uzziel: I say that wisdom does not prevail over foolishness merely by being declared; it must find welcome. But men sometimes refuse wisdom because wisdom's plain dress cannot compete with the verbal finery of

---

129 Isa. 1:10; Ezek. 16:48–56; cf. Dt. 32:32; Jer. 23:14.

130 Isa. 1:11–15.

131 Acts 21:20.

would-be shepherds of the flock. Therefore, I will speak simply and to the point.

I have heard it said that no one can compete with wisdom because wisdom does not compete,[132] and I think there is truth to that. At the same time, Solomon said that wisdom cries out for a hearing,[133] and in compassion for you, brothers, wisdom is compelling me to cry out now to you.

Council members: *Comments.*

Uzziel: Hananiah gave prudent advice to us when he cautioned us to be wary of carefully crafted words which arouse the emotions but cloud the mind. We can be led by our feelings, if we choose, but it is wiser just to believe the holy scriptures. In the days of Isaiah, when our fathers had strayed from God's law, the Almighty spoke to them through the prophet and said, "Come, let us reason together." He did not say, "Come, let us feel excited together." And we can obey the invitation of God to reason together only if we remain within the bounds of Scripture and reject the tantalizing excitement of new ideas and high-sounding philosophy. My words may not excite you, brothers, but they will teach you.

Council members: *Comments.*

Uzziel: I, too, rejoice in the blessing of the Spirit. I was there in the beginning when it fell upon us, and it is truly a precious gift from God, purchased at great price. So, I beg you not to think that I am downplaying the importance of Messiah's sacrifice or of God's testimony of him when I speak in defense of the law. And I must do so, for the law, too, is a precious gift from God. Hananiah's only contention, and mine, is that the law is *still* a blessing. And though it may not arouse in some men the passions which are aroused when reminded of their wonderful experiences in the Spirit, the law remains a holy gift, a stedfast guide, and a friend of the soul – far from a warden over it.

Council members: *Comments.*

Uzziel: Earlier, Barnabas cleverly avoided the truth by changing the subject to a useless discussion of the precise time of the Lord's return. Barnabas left the impression that all the prophets Hananiah quoted were speaking of Gentiles coming to our land to serve God with us only after Jesus returns, but it was wrong for Barnabas to do so.

Hillel: Yes, I was about to bring that up, Uzziel, when you began. Hananiah was right. But continue; I know the prophecy you mean.

Hananiah: I am not sure which prophecy that was, Uzziel.

––––––––––––––––––––

[132] A saying attributed to Lao-Tzu, an ancient Chinese philosopher.
[133] Prov. 1:20–22.

Uzziel: I know, Hananiah. You were thrown off the scent by that worthless discussion about time. But you did not, as you were made to think, misapply the prophecy from Isaiah in which God said that he had made His house a house of prayer for all people. That was not about the end-times, for this is that prophecy in whole: "Thus says the LORD to the eunuchs who are keeping my Sabbaths and holding fast my covenant: In my house and within my walls, I will give them authority and a name better than sons and daughters. I will give them an everlasting name that will not be cut off. And as for the foreigners who join themselves to the LORD, to minister to Him and to be His servants, every one who *keeps His Sabbath rather than profane it and who holds fast my covenant,* them will I also bring to my holy mountain, and I will make them joyful in my house of prayer. Their burnt offerings and their sacrifices will be acceptable on my altar, for my house will be called a house of prayer for all peoples."[134] This is God's promise, and it is for all people at all times, our time and Isaiah's, as well as for the time after our Lord's return. Isaiah was not speaking just of the future, as Barnabas said.

Hillel: Exactly.

Hananiah: That is right, Uzziel. That is right.

Council members: *Comments.*

Uzziel: Note, brothers, at the end of that prophecy, that God promised – and this certainly does have to do with the time of Jesus' return – that He would gather more Gentiles to Israel than those He had gathered to Him in the past.[135] So, Barnabas, Hananiah did not misuse the prophecy.

Barnabas: My comments concerned the other ones Hananiah mentioned, and I should have made it clear that one was excluded. But even so, that prophecy applied to Gentiles who came to Israel before Messiah came, when there was no atonement available without the law; it has nothing to do with our gospel for the Gentiles.

Uzziel: Whether or not God has given you a gospel for the Gentiles is the entire issue, as far as I am concerned. Hear me out now, Barnabas.

Men and brothers, brother Paul brought up the subject of redemption, saying that even the upright in Israel needed a redeemer. I am surprised that none of you noticed the glaring error in that statement. It is true that the righteous in Israel *wanted* the Redeemer to come and that they prayed for God to send him, but at no time in our history were the righteous *in need* of a redeemer. As long as Israel was faithful to God, *He* was their protecter; He blessed them in the city and in the field, and He prospered

---

[134] Isa. 56:4–7.

[135] Isa. 56:8.

everything they set their hands to, so that they needed nothing. This was His promise to Israel from the beginning,[136] and He has never failed to keep that promise to us.

Look what God did for King Hezekiah and for King Josiah when they led this nation back to the law! And when David was old, he prayed for Solomon his son, "The LORD give you insight and understanding, so that when He gives you command over Israel, you might keep the law of the LORD your God. Then you will prosper, when you are careful to carry out the statutes and the judgments which the LORD commanded Moses for Israel."[137] And as long as Solomon obeyed the law, God did prosper him, far above all men.

Council Members: *Comments.*

Uzziel: It was only when Israel forsook the law that the nation needed a redeemer – and it was always a redemption from the foreign enemies which God sent against them to punish them. When God sent the Assyrians to destroy ten of our tribes in the north, what reason is given for such terrible punishment from God? The scriptures say that it was because those tribes had "rejected God's covenant that He made with their fathers. That is why the LORD was angry with Israel and removed them from His sight."[138] And when God sent Nebuchadnezzar to destroy this city and to plunder and burn our temple, and to take our people into captivity, what was it that provoked God to do that? The prophet said it was "because they forsook the covenant of the LORD which He made with them when He brought them out from the land of Egypt."[139] Time and again, God has sent foreign armies into this land to chasten this nation, and time and again, it was for the same reason: failure to keep the law.

Hushai was telling you the truth when he said that God spoke of redemption by the mouth of His prophets hundreds of times, yet not once did He speak of redemption from a sinful nature. What will you do with that truth, brothers? What will you do with the holy scriptures? Do they have no authority over your opinions?

And I would further point out to you that God did not give the law to redeem Israel; that was not the law's purpose. God gave the law for the people whom He had already redeemed. He redeemed Israel from bondage to the Egyptians by the hand of Moses, and then He gave Moses the law to guide the nation. Later, He redeemed Israel from the power of the

---

[136] Dt. 28:1–14.

[137] 1Chron. 22:12–13.

[138] 2Kgs. 17:13–18, excerpts.

[139] Dt. 29:25.

Philistines by the hand of David, and then He gave David the design for the temple and instructions for the new order of service. Those who need a redeemer are those who are in trouble and cannot extract themselves from it, and after God redeems them, He gives them His instructions on how to live. That is how God has always done it, and that is what we should be doing for the Gentiles whom God has redeemed. Now that they have the Spirit of our God, we should give them our God's law so that they might live and worship acceptably with us!

Council members: *Comments.*

Joseph: Uzziel, these are weighty things. Will you allow Barnabas and Paul to respond?

Uzziel: I realize this is taking some time, Joseph, but Barnabas and Paul may take as much time as they wish to respond when I have finished. But I must continue, to deal with a critical point which demands the careful consideration of this Council.

Nahum: Continue, then. We have come together to hear what every man has to say.

Uzziel: Let me ask everyone here a question. Who were the men who lured Israel away from the law, repeatedly, century after century? Who were they whose words were so convincing that they were able to make God's people forget the bitter lessons of previous generations of rebels? I will tell you who they were; they were trusted leaders and beloved brothers who had drifted away from the sure testimonies of the law and imagined that they had seen a better way. Many of them claimed to have received a new revelation. That was certainly true of the friendly old prophet from Bethel who deceived the man of God and brought upon him deadly wrath.[140]

Regardless of the details of false prophets' messages over the years, the result of their teachings was always – always! – that Israel was less obedient to the law and more like the heathen. That was the single result of every new doctrine about how better to serve God. Those false doctrines may have differed from one generation to the next, but the result was always the same: less devotion to the law and more fellowship with uncircumcised Gentiles.

Levi: This is truth Uzziel is telling us, brothers! You know this is the true history of our people!

Uzziel: We need not examine and debate the details of every false doctrine that comes against the faith; we need only ask the false prophet one thing: what about the holy law of God? Should we keep it or not?

---

[140] 1Kgs. 13:11–24.

The wise have always known that whatever is not of the law is false, no matter how truthful false teachers sound. Whatever any man proclaims that is not the law is false! That is the standard, and to debate scriptures and doctrines with such men is vain. Wisdom does not do that; it has no interest in debate or in winning quarrels. Wisdom's concern is solely the well-being of good men.

Council members: *Comments*.

Uzziel: No one denies that Barnabas and Paul have had genuine experiences with God and are well-versed in the scriptures. I am as thankful as anyone here for the mercy God has had on them, and on us all. But let us reason together, brothers. Ask yourselves, which false prophet in our history has *not* had genuine experiences with God or been well-versed in the scriptures? Which false prophet in our history did not have a real connection with God before he became false? Search the scriptures. The title "false prophet" is not given to any man that was not first a servant of God. None of the heathen are called false prophets because they are dogs and blind from the moment of their birth; they have no relationship with God to begin with, and therefore, cannot be false to Him.

Wasn't Balaam a true prophet before he became false to God and sold himself to serve Balak, King of Moab? Had he not had genuine experiences with God, and heard His voice? Yet, look at the damage that he did to this nation when he became a false prophet to the One who had made him great![141] And the elders of Jezreel were men of Israel, well-versed in the law, but they became false to God and sold themselves to Jezebel, craftily using their knowledge of the law to justify the murder of righteous Naboth and his sons![142] And Caiaphas and his father-in-law Annas were highly regarded, but they were false to our God, and look at what they did to Jesus!

It is dangerous to know much without knowing God. That is why David warned his son not just to get gain, but with all his getting, to get understanding![143]

Council members: *Comments*.

Uzziel: Men and brothers, spiritual experiences are only as good as our understanding of them, and the holy scriptures are only as trustworthy as the men who use them. Any gift from God can become a curse if it is misused. From the lips of deceived ministers, holy scriptures are transformed into a deadly poison.

---

[141] Balaam's story is found in Numbers 22 through 24.

[142] 1Kgs. 21:7–13; 2Kgs. 9:26.

[143] Prov. 4:7.

Council members: *Comments.*

But even at that, brothers, even at that! Leaving aside Barnabas and Paul's questionable use of a few scriptures, tell me, how many of the prophets did the well-versed Paul quote when he said that everyone who obeyed the law needed a redeemer, or when he said that all we need is our spiritual experiences, for only what Jesus does for our souls will save us? If there were any such scripture, do you think he would have not mentioned it? Surely, if his doctrine were of God, the prophets would have foretold such a thing! Surely, there would be a myriad of scriptures promising that Messiah would be so glorious that faith in him releases men from the duty to obey the law of God. But no! Paul used no scripture to show his doctrine because there is no such scripture! And there is no such scripture because the *scriptures* are true, not Paul!

Council members: *Comments.*

Uzziel: I listened carefully, brothers, to Paul and Barnabas; this Council gave them time, as it did Hananiah, to fully explain their doctrine. And what did we hear from them but a new philosophy, a clever slant on a few scriptures, and long speeches based on claims of a new revelation! We heard that we are born with a sinful nature, based upon the plain words of . . . no prophet. And we heard that God's holy law could do nothing to change us, based upon the plain words of . . . no prophet. And we heard of becoming a new kind of creature, and of a new kind of law based upon the plain words of . . . no prophet. And how does Paul know such things without the law or the prophets? Why, he and Barnabas know such things because they possess a new kind of knowledge!

Council members: *Comments.*

Uzziel: I do not accept that kind of doctrine, no matter how thrilling it may sound, and my refusal is based upon the solid rock of God's law and God's prophets. Eloquent speeches mean nothing to me; the eloquence of the simple truth of God's law is what thrills me. And I praise God for that holy law! I bless His holy name!

Hushai, Hillel, Lamech, Levi, Eli, Hilkiah, Nadab: *Amen! Praise God! Etc.*

Uzziel: And now, brothers, if I must, I will be silent, but I am in earnest concerning the welfare of those who believe, and there is much more to say.

Hushai, Hillel, Lamech, Levi, Eli, Hilkiah, Nadab: *We would hear more! Go on, Uzziel! Etc.*

Levi: I want to hear what else Uzziel has to say!

Jacobus: Barnabas, would you speak now? Or Paul?

Barnabas: We can wait, Jacobus.

Paul: Yes, we would hear Uzziel out.

Jacobus: Then, Uzziel, what else do you have to say?

Uzziel: I reject Paul's claim that the knowledge of God was completely unknown to all men, even the most righteous of men, before Messiah came. That is false. It was the knowledge of the Son of God that was hidden beforetime, not the knowledge of God Himself. Even Balaam had the knowledge of God, for when he prophesied for King Balak in Moab, it is written – it is written, brothers! – that his was "the voice of him who hears the words of God and possesses knowledge of the Most High!"[144] It is written, brothers! It is written! Or does that not thrill you? Where is our allegiance? To God or to Paul?

Council members: *Comments*.

Uzziel: And King David, who himself knew God, told his son Solomon, "If you cry out for discernment and lift your voice for understanding, then you will find the knowledge of God."[145] Now, Paul, you may think that this was vain advice for the young man, that no one could know God before Messiah came. However, when Solomon ascended to the throne and prayed for wisdom and knowledge, what was *God's* response? He said that the wisdom and knowledge he prayed for, the wisdom and knowledge that his father David counseled him to seek, would be granted to him![146] Furthermore, why would God have lamented through Hosea – twice – that there was no knowledge of God in the land,[147] except that the knowledge of God *could have* and *should have* been in this land? And after righteous King Josiah died, God said of him, "He judged the cause of the afflicted and poor. Then, it went well. Is this not the knowledge of me? says the LORD."[148]

Our righteous fathers possessed the knowledge of God; to suggest otherwise is contrary to everything the scriptures tell us. It is based upon a false claim of a secret kind of knowledge which denies the plain truth of the scriptures, and I do not want it! Why would I? And why do some of you?

Council members: *Comments*.

Uzziel: And as for how much glory and power Messiah has, or even how much power God Himself has, that is a subject for vain philosophical

---

[144] Num. 24:16a.

[145] Prov. 2:3, 5b.

[146] 2Chron. 1:12a.

[147] Hos. 4:1; 6:6.

[148] Jer. 22:16.

speculation, something the Athenians would enjoy discussing over wine, as they relax on their couches after gorging themselves at a banquet. Jesus told us that all power in heaven and earth has been given to him,[149] and that is all we need to know. God's power cannot be measured, and how much of it now is given to Jesus is not the issue. The issue is, how has God chosen to *use* His power? God has always had the choice to save by His power alone, as Paul says He is doing now. He could have saved Israel without giving us the law if He had desired to do so. But what did God choose to do? He chose to save us by His power *and the law!*

Council members: *Comments.*

Levi: . . . which is what Isaiah said: "To the law and to the Spirit!" That is the only true gospel!

Uzziel: Surely, God is in heaven this moment, grieving over this senseless division among us, saying to this Assembly what He said to Moses: "How long will *you* refuse to keep my commandments and my laws?"[150] I would suggest that we stop right now and pray for the mercies of heaven, except that I have not forgotten the warning of Solomon, who said: "He who turns his ear away from hearing the law, even his prayer is an abomination."[151] How can we ask the God of the law to guide us, when we are here arguing about whether or not men should keep it? Would you ask a shepherd to help you steal his own sheep?

Bartholomew: Uzziel, that's enough.

Council members: *Comments.*

Uzziel: Were you mesmerized, brothers, with the crafty use of a few scriptures?

Andrew: Brother Uzziel . . .

Uzziel: Were you so swept up in the power of great, swelling words that your minds went altogether numb? Did you not ask yourselves how it could be that even if Messiah Jesus had stayed with us a thousand years, we would never have been changed, as Paul said? Or when he said that we need only the law and the Messiah that are within us, were you so thrilled that you forgot the law that we read daily and the Messiah who is sitting at God's right hand? After all, *they are both outside of us!* God's Messiah being in my heart does not mean I no longer need the Messiah who is at God's right hand! And God's law being in my heart does not mean that I no longer need the law that I read every day of my life! Tell

---

[149] Mt. 28:18.

[150] Ex. 16:28.

[151] Prov. 28:9.

me, brothers, if we need only what is inside of us, why do you worship God, who is outside of you?

Council members: *Comments.*

Jacobus: Uzziel, this is too much. It is time for you . . .

Uzziel: This new doctrine is useless philosophical babble, the pabulum of spiritual infants! I cannot fathom how such specious arguments, though from the mouths of friends, could blind such a gathering of godly men – men with whom I have labored many years now, striving for the faith and suffering for the faith with you! Barnabas is not the only one here who sold all that he owned and laid the proceeds at your feet. He was following the example of many of us who were here before him.

Council members: *Comments.*

Uzziel: And I am not complaining about having done that; I am glad I did it. The Lord has rewarded me many times over for it, as he promised to do. I am only warning this assembly to beware. I know how highly most of you esteem Barnabas and Paul, but do you think Israel in old time did not esteem the men who led them astray? Do you think false prophets were the rabble of the streets? No! Sons of Belial have never deceived this people; the leaders of Israel's apostasies from God were always men whom the people respected. The men who persuaded the people in the wilderness to turn against Moses, were "leaders of the congregation, chosen men of the Assembly, men of reputation"[152] – Moses' own cousin, Korah, being chief among them.[153] God's people have never been and never will be deceived, but by men they love and trust.

Council members: *Comments.*

Uzziel: Let the thrilling stories that Barnabas and Paul tell of the miracles they performed among the heathen be true. I applaud it. But if you look to miracles as proof of God's approval, remember why God said He miraculously brought the law down from heaven with such thunderous, fiery darkness: "I am coming to you in a thick cloud," He said, "so that the people may hear when I speak with you and may believe in you forever."[154] And now, is Israel to cease believing in Moses, and follow instead these men who perform miracles but declare a gospel contrary to Moses and the prophets, and even to Messiah's own example?

Council members: *Comments.*

Nahum: Let that be enough now, Uzziel.

---

[152] Num. 16:2.

[153] Num. 16:1 with Ex. 6:16–21. Also see 1Chron. 6:16–22.

[154] Ex. 19:9.

Uzziel: I knew before I came that it would be this way. If Hananiah had not insisted that I come, I would have stayed at home instead of wasting my time here. Hananiah and the others told me what Paul and Barnabas did to them before the whole assembly in Antioch, and now, having seen and heard their heresy for myself, I will have no more of it. The blood of the Gentiles will be on your hands, not mine! [*Uzziel walks out.*]

Hananiah: Uzziel, no. Wait!

Levi: I go with Uzziel!

Council members: *Levi, don't leave! Come back! Etc.*

Levi: Uzziel has never taught me wrongly, and I trust him more than you all! You men have become blind! [*Levi walks out.*]

The Council Deals with Uzziel's Departure

Daniel: [*after a few moments of quiet*] Brothers, God does not make men right who insist that they already are. We must, every one of us, be open always to the possibility of being wrong; otherwise we can never be made right. Jesus said that he came not to heal the healthy but the sick, and not to call the righteous but sinners to repentance.[155] And he told some that because they claimed to see, they would remain blind.[156]

Hananiah: Perhaps I should not have prevailed upon Uzziel to come with me, but he is so much more capable than I . . .

Jacobus: You did no wrong, Hananiah. Uzziel was as welcome as anyone here.

Council members: *Amen. Yes, he was. Etc.*

Maschil: But why would brother Uzziel have to be persuaded to come? I felt honored to be a part of this meeting, just to sit here among such men of God.

Hananiah: Micah, he is your pupil. It might be better if you . . .

Micah: It is difficult, Maschil, to explain. I wouldn't want to hurt anyone here.

Paul: I will tell it.

Jacobus: You don't need to, Paul.

Paul: I should be the one.

Maschil: What is it?

Lamech: Go ahead and tell him, Paul! I want to hear you say it!

Jacobus: You don't need to, Paul.

---

[155] Mk. 2:17.

[156] Jn. 9:41.

Paul: I should. Maschil, some years ago, brother Uzziel had a dear son, Samuel, whom he loved very much, and who loved the Lord. At the time, as you know, I was adamantly against the faith.

Maschil: Yes.

Paul: There was a meeting of believers in Bethlehem, and when I learned of it, I reported it to the authorities, and I went with them to arrest them. Uzziel and Samuel were there, and when Samuel saw his father being handled roughly, he protested and was struck down by one of the officers. Uzziel pleaded with us for him, but we mocked him and threw them all into prison. Samuel never recovered. He died not long after.

Jacobus: Brother Paul, no man in this place holds your former conduct against you. You did all that in the ignorance of unbelief.

Council members: *Comments.*

Paul: That is why Hananiah had to persuade Uzziel to come. Uzziel knew I would be here, and, well, you can understand. You have a young son.

Maschil: I didn't know, brother Paul. I am sorry. And to be truthful, I don't know who I feel the more hurt for, you or Uzziel. Him, for his awful loss, or you, for the burden of that memory.

Paul: Thank you, Maschil. You have a kind heart. It is Jesus alone who enables me to live with the things I did in my unbelief. Jesus has been for me what he was for guilty King David, "the lifter up of my head."[157]

Hananiah: I would not have brought it up, Paul.

Maschil: I regret asking why . . .

Jacobus: No, Maschil. You did nothing wrong. Every man here is ashamed of some past deed that would grieve and humiliate him if it was publicly aired.

Micah: It has been over ten years since that happened, Maschil, but it is still very difficult for Uzziel.

Hananiah: When I asked Uzziel to come with me, I knew that his reticence to come was because he didn't know how seeing Paul would make him feel. Samuel was a sweet young man.

Maschil: That is why brother Uzziel did not come to hear Paul and Barnabas when they first arrived and testified in the Assembly, isn't it?

Jacobus: Yes.

Silas: Or at least, that is what Uzziel thinks.

Maschil: What do you mean, Silas?

---

[157] Ps. 3:3.

Silas: I mean that Uzziel is not the only man here who lost someone in persecutions in which Paul took part. Can you tell me, Maschil, based on attitudes toward Paul that you have seen today, who they are who lost someone they loved?

Maschil: No. I would not have suspected that, from what I have seen.

Silas: So, the issue is not so much what Paul did in the past, but what Jesus is doing for the rest of us, now.

Hilkiah: Do *you* sit in judgment on Uzziel, a righteous man and a great scholar?

Silas: A man walking in the Spirit judges everything, Hilkiah. But I will show you what I am saying. You recall that Eliam was one of David's elite warriors, and a godly and faithful man.[158]

Hilkiah: Yes, I know that.

Silas: And you may recall that Eliam was also Bathsheba's father.[159]

Hilkiah: Yes.

Silas: Then, try to imagine, Hilkiah, how Eliam must have felt when he learned that even though David had forced himself on Eliam's daughter and then murdered her righteous husband so that he could keep her – God forgave David contrary to the law and kept him on the throne.

Council members: *Comments.*

Silas: Where was Eliam's justice, demanded by the law, for his abused daughter and the deceitful murder of Uriah? Can you imagine the pain that David's sin had brought upon that good man, Eliam, and his family? And after God restored David to the throne, do you think you could have bowed to the king as before, the way Eliam must have done? Could you have humbled yourself before the man who ruined your sweet daughter's life and murdered her godly husband?

Council members: *Comments.*

Hilkiah: I think I could have bowed.

Silas: Perhaps. Perhaps you could have.

Hilkiah: Whom God honors, we must honor.

Silas: That is certainly true. But it is easier to imagine that we would do what is right than to actually do it when our hearts have been torn to shreds by someone's evil deeds. At any rate, I am confident that even if you had bowed, you would not have taken much pleasure in doing so.

But this brings me to my answer for you about brother Uzziel. Ahithophel was, as Hananiah said earlier, David's wisest counsellor.

Hilkiah: Yes.

---

[158] 2Sam. 8:34. The complete list is found in 2Samuel 23:8–39.

[159] 2Sam. 11:3.

Silas: But he was also Eliam's father, Bathsheba's grandfather, and when the happiness of Eliam's family, that is, of his own family, was destroyed by David's sin, he turned on David and helped Absalom to seize the kingdom. Now, Hilkiah, that shrewd counselor Ahithophel was wiser than to join such a rebellion, but his pain blinded him because, to be blunt, his grief went deeper into his heart than did his faith in God.

Hillel: Are you saying that Uzziel . . .

Silas: I am saying that if God forgives a sinner, and we do not, then we have set ourselves up as judges, not over men, but over God.

Council members: *Comments.*

Daniel: Brother Hilkiah, If we do not humble ourselves to lay our pain down at the feet of Jesus, if we do not yield our pain to the healing balm of his Spirit, our pain will ferment into a blinding poison, the poison of bitterness, and the souls of many have been defiled by it. This world has no power to hurt us so deeply that Jesus cannot bind up our wounds and make us happy again, and he will do it if we are only willing to be healed.

Silas: Earth has no pain so great that heaven cannot heal it if we lay our burden down at Jesus' feet.

Paul: Nor is there any earthly shame so great that Jesus cannot lift up our head. Jesus gave me hope and made me feel like living again after I learned what great evils I had done.

Council members begin singing a hymn:

Daniel:
> The holy Spirit has come!
>> With blood, he purchased it, God's Son.
> From heaven's portal came life immortal,
>> the healing morsel of God's Son.

Silas:
> The broken-hearted, he heals,
>> and broken bodies by God's will.
> Messiah Savior! He's faithful ever;
>> he'll fail us never: God's Son.

Daniel, Silas, Paul, Matthew:
> No power ever (*we were as dead*)
>> can from us sever (*we could not see*)
> the love of Jesus (*the life he gave us*),
>> God's holy One (*has made us free*).
> He is the glory (the Father's glory)
>> of heaven's story (*has made us new*).
> Come and adore him (*we're his alone*): God's Son.

Paul: [*during musical interlude*]: There was no forgiveness in the law for my sins, but through His Son, God had mercy on me without the law! Jesus will create a virgin's heart in the breast of a harlot if she believes in him, law or no law!

Paul [*sings*]:

> The vilest sinner may come,
>> God's kingdom enter with God's Son.
> The deepest stain within upon the souls of men,
>> he washes clean from sin, God's Son.

Matthew:

> When we come to his grace, God's Son.
>> He makes for us a place, God's Son.
> His mercy makes us wise and keeps us satisfied
>> to be the waiting bride of God's Son.

Daniel, Silas, Paul, Matthew:

> No power ever (*we were as dead*)
>> can from us sever (*we could not see*)
> the love of Jesus (*the life he gave us*),
>> God's holy One (*has made us free*).
> He is the glory (the Father's glory)
>> of heaven's story (*has made us new*).
> Come bow before him (*we're his alone*): God's Son.[160]

Barnabas: It doesn't matter who or where we are; it only matters who and where Jesus is. And who and where is he? He is in heaven, sitting at the Father's right hand, possessing all power over all Creation, and he is able not only to save to the uttermost, but also to heal to the uttermost the souls who come to him, no matter what their past has been. He gives sinners more than new hope for the future; he gives men a new past, with Abraham as their father and Sarah as their mother! Jesus makes all things new, I tell you! There is no corruption of body or soul from which he will not deliver us! And that is why it is wrong, Maschil, for a man to stubbornly remain broken; Jesus is willing and able to heal and to restore.

Jacobus: Who has ever been more unjustly abused than Jesus? And yet, while writhing in agony on the cross, he prayed earnestly for his tormenters. Then, who are we to be bitter against anyone who causes us to suffer, as if Jesus deserved his abuse, but we do not? Brothers, no one in Christ is a victim! In him, we have conquered this Creation and everything in it!

---

[160] "God's Son" by John D. Clark, Sr.

Council members: *Comments.*

Jacobus: We have not seen the happy Uzziel we once knew since the death of his son. His son's death was very tragic and unjust, and yes, brother Paul had a hand in it. But if God forgives a sinner, he is completely forgiven. And if God gives him a new life, that sinner's past is no more – except in hearts made bitter by unyielded pain.

Silas: It may yet be, brothers, that God will forgive Uzziel for clinging to his hurt instead of surrendering his broken heart to the healing touch of Jesus. I, for one, believe that in the resurrection, King David and Bathsheba's murdered husband will embrace one another like long-lost brothers. And I believe that if Uzziel will surrender his broken heart to Jesus and not nurse the bitterness that now rules it, he will run to find brother Paul and embrace him with his whole heart.

Council members: *Comments.*

Silas: Let us, then, pray for Uzziel, that he will humble himself to the God who loves him, for if he does, then God will be for him what He was for David, and what He is for brother Paul: the lifter up of his head!

Council members: *Comments..*

Silas: Let us, then, pray for Uzziel, that he will humble himself to the God who loves him, and God will be for him what He was for David, and what He is for brother Paul: the lifter up of his head.

Council members: *Comments.*

Daniel: We can control the spirits of men no more than we can control the weather; all such things are in God's hands, and so, we labor each day in whatever weather comes. It may be that God will relieve Uzziel of his stormy disposition, but we have no control over that. Let us who are still here continue now to labor for the unity that Messiah prayed for us to have.

Council members: *Comments.*

Hillel

Hillel: Amen, Daniel. Let us do so. Now, brothers, I would speak.

Council members: *Comments.*

Hillel: [*Hillel rises.*] I sympathize with any man for the sins he has committed, for sin breaks communion with God, and eternal Judgment is coming. I also rejoice for any man who obtains pardon from God for his sins, and I am sure that Uzziel feels as I do, that you men misjudge him. Knowing him as I do, I say that he walked out of this Council, not because he prefers bitterness over the help of God, but because he deemed it pointless to continue arguing for the truth. God forbid that he is right about that, for if this conversation is indeed pointless, no hope is left for this nation.

Council members: *Comments.*

Hillel: I neither condone nor condemn Uzziel for leaving. He is free to come or go as he will. And as for the things he said about the law, I judge them to be undeniably true. I understand his grief and his frustration at the resistance to the truth that he felt from so many in this room. And lest there be any confusion about what I mean when I say "the truth", I will remind you of what David said to God: "Your law is truth."[161]

Now, as much as I respect brother Daniel, I cannot agree with the opinion that a man's use of holy Scripture may or may not be relevant when defending the truth. I believe that the holy scriptures are eternally true and that Jesus showed us to do as they say, and I can yield to no philosophy or new revelation that would turn me from them. We should serve God in the gifts He has given, and not forsake those gifts in order to follow after men who claim to have a deeper – and different – understanding from that of Moses and the prophets. I will give you an example of the great need for the proper use of Scripture.

God did say the words, "Every man is brutish in knowledge," as brother Paul testified. And Paul did well to repeat that phrase just as Jeremiah said it. However, God was speaking of men who construct idols, not to the entire human race! What God actually said was this: "Every man is brutish in knowledge; every refiner is put to shame by his idol, for his molded image is a lie."[162] God never condemned all men as brutish. He condemned even the best men among the Gentiles as brutish,[163] and He condemned our people as brutish when they forsook the law and lived like Gentiles. But God was condemning only the wicked among our people, not all of them, for He said through David, "Understand, *you* brutish among the people! And *you* fools, when will *you* ever understand?"[164] Solomon, in his great wisdom, said that the man who hates reproof is brutish but that a good man elicits favor from the LORD.[165] He did not say that both good and evil men are brutish, the way Paul teaches. The scriptures tell us plainly that it is the fool who is brutish and has no knowledge, not the wise.[166]

---

[161] Ps. 119:142.
[162] Jer. 10:14 and 51:17.
[163] Cf. Isa. 19:11.
[164] Ps. 94:8.
[165] Prov. 12:1b–2.
[166] Ps. 92:6.

So, you see now, men and brothers, the value of the scriptures in putting crafty doctrines to the test. I thank God for providing us the tool to do that, and I will use it!

Council members: *Comments.*

Hillel: Can you not see, men and brothers, that man's brutishness is the very reason God gave us the law? For the law lifts us up out of our beastly ignorance and teaches us righteousness and wisdom. The knowledge of God revealed to us in the law is the very thing that makes Israel superior to the brutish Gentiles, and God has commanded us not to be like them! Yet, Hananiah and the others are condemned as false because they encouraged the heathen to forsake their brutishness and join us in our God-given glory, the law, which makes Israel, Israel.

Council members: *Comments.*

Hillel: I do not deny that we know God far better now than even righteous men knew Him before Messiah Jesus sent us the Spirit. But this more perfect knowledge of God does not negate the knowledge of God that our fathers possessed. And they *did* possess it, for the scriptures tell us that there are but two groups that do not know God: the heathen[167] and the wicked among our own nation.[168] Based on that, brothers, I have a question that I would like to put to this Council, and it is this: have you considered that if righteous men of old did not know God, as Paul teaches, then when the prophets prayed for God's wrath to fall upon those who did not know Him,[169] were they not praying for wrath to fall upon the righteous, too? There is no need to answer; I would ask only that you think about it.

Council members: *Comments.*

Hillel: In the days of the prophets, seeing the wicked among His people, God said, "They bend their tongue, as they bend their bow, for deceit, and they are not strong for truth in the land. Indeed, they proceed from evil to evil, and they do not know me, says the LORD."[170] Now, brothers, even a child can understand that if God was grieved with those who were doing evil, then they could have and should have been doing good. And if He was grieved with liars, then they could have and should have been speaking the truth. So then, if He was grieved with those in Israel who did not know Him, then they could have and should have known Him!

Council members: *Comments.*

---

[167] Ps. 79:6; Ex. 5:2.
[168] Isa. 26:10.
[169] Ps. 79:6; Jer. 10:25.
[170] Jer. 9:3.

Hillel: We believe in revelation; we know God still speaks. But, brothers, true revelation today does not contradict yesterday's truth. Moses' law did not make Abraham's circumcision void, but incorporated it into itself. God's commandments build upon one another, brothers, and justify one another. They do not contradict and cancel out each other.

Hananiah: Barnabas, my dear friend, your strange doctrine is not the thing that touched your heart and brought you here from your native Crete. Cease from it! Return to the faith you once embraced, the faith that was once for all delivered to the saints!

Barnabas: What touched me, Hananiah, and brought me here the first time was the revelation of God's Messiah, and I wish you could see that it is another revelation of God concerning His Messiah that has brought me back to you.

Eliezar: What has Barnabas done wrong, Hananiah, if he has heard from God?

Elkanah: To condemn the just is ungodly.

Benjamin: Then why did Barnabas and Paul condemn Hananiah and the others who went to Antioch to help the ignorant Gentiles?

Nahum: Patience, young men. God will make it known who has erred and who has not. Be still and allow Hillel to finish. If Paul and Barnabas have a response to the things he and Uzziel, or these other brothers, have said, you may learn much from it.

Hillel: I will be just a moment longer, Nahum. Men and brothers, it may be that Uzziel's discernment is better than ours, and this meeting is indeed pointless; that remains to be seen. But for now, I will attempt to hold up the sacred banner of God's law against these strong winds, since his weary hands could no longer do it. However, what is certainly pointless is for you men to waste more time speculating about Uzziel's motives. It will be wiser for you to consider the truths Uzziel spoke before he left. To some of you, such a conversation may seem dull compared to engaging in speculation about someone's imagined spiritual faults, but searching for truth concerning the gospel holds the potential of leading us to unity – if that is truly your goal today. What say you to that suggestion, brothers? [*Hillel sits.*]

Council members: *Comments.*

Joseph: I agree, brother Hillel. No one can deny that Uzziel summed up well the case for the requirement of Moses' law for the Gentiles and that he deserves an answer. Would that he had stayed to hear one, but we who are still here will hear the response of Paul and Barnabas.

Council members: *Comments.*

Daniel: First, however, I will comment upon a truth which Uzziel brought to our attention, namely, that only those who sound right are in a position to mislead men. Uzziel stated that Barnabas and Paul sounded right but that they they did not use many scriptures, and therefore, they are misleading those they teach. However, I caution this Council to note that Uzziel also sounded right, but he *did* use many scriptures. And since both sides cannot be right, "sounding right" must not be the measure of truth, whether using many scriptures or few.

Council members: *Comments.*

Daniel: I ask you to note, brothers, that in his day, Noah had no scripture which could confirm for men God's unheard-of command to build an ark. All he could do for his generation was to repeat to them what God had privately said to him.[171] And father Abraham had no scripture to confirm God's unheard-of command to forsake his homeland and kinsmen to go to a place which God would only later show him.[172] Nor did Abraham have any scripture to justify God's unheard-of command to circumcise his sons on the eighth day;[173] he had only a word from God, which, as with Noah, came to him alone, out of all the men on earth. Likewise, Moses had no scripture by which he might confirm for Israel that the commandments he received while alone on the mountain with God[174] had truly been spoken to him by God. And King David had no scripture to confirm for others the revelation that God had chosen Jerusalem as the one acceptable place of worship,[175] or for his revelation concerning the new order for temple worship.[176] So, my friends, the absence of scripture references does not necessarily equate to the absence of truth. God does not use scriptures; He creates them. He does not need scriptures to justify His commands; when He speaks, He is His own authority.

Council members: *Comments.*

Daniel: With a living God, the only truth that exists is what He is saying today, regardless of what He said yesterday, for God guides us according to what we need, not according to what we once needed. Were it not so, Jesus would not have exhorted us to ask God for daily bread.[177] The Word of God is not a dead thing, carved into a stone or written in a book

---

[171] Gen. 6:13–21.

[172] Gen. 12:1.

[173] Gen. 17:12.

[174] Ex. 19:18–21; Dt. 5:5.

[175] Ps. 132:13. Cf. 2Chron. 6:4–6.

[176] 1Chron. 28:11–20.

[177] Mt. 6:11; Lk. 11:3.

so that only the literate may know it. The Word of God is the Messiah that came forth from His bosom and dwelt among us.

Yes, Messiah Jesus is the life which was in the beginning with God, and God chose our time to send that life to walk among us! We were chosen to hear with our ears the voice of him who made the stars, and to see with our eyes the one whom God had hidden from all previous generations, and to touch with our hands him who has now touched our hearts and sanctified us! To have that life living within us, leading us, is to be perfect as our heavenly Father is perfect, not as Abraham, or as Job, or as Moses was perfect, and we need nothing more than that.

Council members: *Comments.*

Nahum: Amen, Daniel. And now, Barnabas and Paul, what will you say to these men?

God's Kind of Life

Paul: I will answer them, sir.

Nahum: Then may God give you wisdom, son, for as you have seen, it will be difficult to convince some that the Gentiles are free from our law.

Paul: Yes, that much is very clear.

Nahum: And if our Jewish brothers are not persuaded of your doctrine, and yet, the believing Gentiles are persuaded, then there will be a lasting division in the household of God, and Messiah's heart will break.

Paul: That is true, and it is a pain which I would spare our Savior. He has suffered enough.

Council members: *Comments.*

Nahum: Go ahead now, son.

Paul: [*Paul rises.*] Men and brothers, Uzziel and Hillel have scoffed at the notion that the Spirit has brought a new kind of knowledge into our hearts; however, the knowledge which righteous men of old possessed was only the knowledge of things *about* God. It is akin to the knowledge that some animals have, which men can use in training them to obey commands, the same way men are trained by laws to act as if they are good, even if they are not. That is not the knowledge of God. If Balaam had truly known God, as Uzziel thinks he did, he would not have prayed a second time, hoping to change God's mind and allow him to prophesy against Israel.[178] And the wisdom that Solomon asked God for was only the wisdom to be a wise ruler of God's people, for he said, "Give me now

---

[178] This part of Balaam's story is found in Numbers 22:5–35.

wisdom and knowledge, that I might go out and come in before this people, for who can judge this nation of yours, which is so great?"[179] Moreover, had Solomon possessed the true knowledge of God, he would not have taken seven hundred wives and built altars for some of them to use for the sacrifice of their own children – Solomon's children![180] And the lack of knowledge in this land which grieved God's heart was the lack of knowledge of Moses' law, which, again, was only knowledge *about* God, by which men were trained to act as if they knew Him. I say again, the law could never give us the true knowledge of God, for God had hidden all true wisdom and knowledge in His Son, and no one on earth ever saw or heard such wisdom and knowledge until the Son came to earth with it.

Council members: *Comments*.

Paul: I agree with Uzziel and Hillel, brothers, on this point, that there is little or no benefit in doctrinal debate, for the kingdom of God is not in word, but in power. However, fellowship in the light of God is worth striving for, and to that end, I testify to all men of the revelation Jesus gave to me. After that, God decides who will believe it and who will not.

God produced the scriptures, brothers; He is not subject to them. Nor is He limited by them. The Spirit of truth did not come from the law; the law came from the Spirit of truth. Brother Micah, you said, as David once did,[181] that the law of the LORD is perfect, and so it is, but the Spirit which Jesus died for us to have is beyond the perfection that David knew, or that any man knew from the beginning of the world until Messiah poured out the Spirit from on high. The Spirit of God is beyond all earthly perfection.

Abraham was perfect before God;[182] still, Abraham rejoiced to see Jesus' day,[183] not because he longed for Messiah to completely subdue the nations and exalt Israel, but because he longed for the kind of life that would completely subdue him and exalt God. Noah was also perfect with God,[184] but did he not long for the baptism of life that saves us, which his ark foreshadowed? All the righteous men of old died longing for the Son of God to come, without knowing that God even had a Son, or that it was the Son of God for which they longed. They only felt their need of a

---

179 2Chron. 1:10.

180 1Kgs. 11:3–7.

181 Ps. 19:7.

182 Gen. 17:1–2.

183 Jn. 8:56.

184 Gen. 6:9.

different kind of life, a truly holy life, and they did not know that God would one day share His holy life with those who believed in His Son.

In the Spirit, brothers, *all things* are new, not just the knowledge that is in it. In the Spirit, we experience a new kind of birth into a new Israel, in which there is not only a new and eternal kind of righteousness, but also a new kind of wisdom and goodness, and – hear me, my circumcised brothers, a new kind of circumcision and a new law – the law of the Spirit of truth which I preach and by which we rightly judge all things, but are rightly judged by no man.

Council members: *Comments.*

Paul: God judged Job to be "a perfect and upright man" before He sent Satan to afflict him.[185] But God did not allow Satan or anyone else to know His purpose, that He had determined to drive righteous Job by terrible afflictions beyond his perfection to taste a new kind of humility, the kind of humility found only in the life of God. Yes, by every measure of righteousness found on earth, Job was perfect, but when God drove Job beyond perfection to taste of His kind of humility, Job cried out, "I despise myself, and I repent in dirt and ashes,"[186] for he sensed the wretchedness of his imperfect fleshly nature and was overwhelmed by it. He did not know that God had a Son and that God's Son would one day come to earth and pay the price for us to receive God's kind of life – the only cure for man's sinfulness.

Council members: *Comments.*

Paul: Consider, brothers, that according to the law which God gave Moses, neither murderers nor adulterers could by any means be forgiven, but had to die.[187] They could not pay a fine in order to escape execution,[188] nor did the law provide any sacrifice for the atonement of such sins. Even if a murderer fled to God's altar and laid hold of it, begging for mercy, the judges were to drag him away and kill him.[189] Therefore, when David committed adultery with Bathsheba and then murdered Uriah,[190] the law that David loved provided him with no means of escape from the penalty for his sins. Nevertheless, God sent the prophet Nathan

---

[185] Job 1:8.
[186] Job 42:6.
[187] Num. 35:16–21; Lev. 20:10.
[188] Num 35:30–31.
[189] Ex. 21:14.
[190] 2Sam. 11:1–4, 14–17.

to David, who told him, "The LORD has put away your sin; you shall not die."[191]

Council members: *Comments.*

Paul: By what authority did God forgive David when the law forbade it? I will tell you by what authority – His own! And in forgiving David, God was revealing to David and to all Israel that in Him is mercy beyond the perfection of the law, for He Himself is beyond the law, so far beyond the law that most of Israel refused to believe it, and rebelled against the King,[192] thinking to defend the integrity of the law against a king who would not keep it. They were men like Uzziel, and like some of you, who did not believe in mercy beyond the law, for you, like those of David's time, demand the law be enforced even when God does not enforce it! You are the Absaloms of our time, rebelling against the Son of David, thinking to defend the integrity of the law against a God who does not keep it!

Council members: *Comments.*

Hillel: No man can be silent at such talk! Uzziel is a good man!

Paul: You'll be silent a little longer. I have been silent long enough.

Hananiah: Wait, Hillel, I beg you.

Paul: It angered the nation, brothers, when God touched David with His kind of mercy, just as Uzziel and these other men are angered by my gospel that proclaims it. But God was with David, and he prevailed. And God is with me, and I will prevail!

Council members: *Comments.*

Paul: From the beginning, God kept His kind of life hidden with His Son, but now, God's life, with its unlawful mercy, is revealed, and men may now be forgiven of sins which the law did not forgive. I myself have been shown that mercy, for I partook in the persecution and killing of God's saints. I am living proof of my gospel, and so are the uncircumcised Gentiles who have believed and repented, for they have also received the life of God and are walking in the light of Messiah Jesus.

Council members: *Comments.*

Paul: Now speak, Hillel. I give you room. Do you demand that the law be kept at all times, by all people, in all circumstances, or do you not? What would you have done to David, or to me?   You men told the believing Gentiles in Antioch they would be damned without your law, and you would have damned David for the same ungodly reason. [*Paul sits.*]

---

[191] 2Sam. 12:13.

[192] 2Sam. 15:1ff.

Council members: *Comments.*

Hillel: Whatever any man would have felt or done a thousand years ago, only God can say, not you, brother Paul. Our time is now, and on this day, I will not allow your distortion of the meaning of God's grace on the ignorant to stand! Defense of the truth is condemned by those who pervert it, but God will uphold those who uphold His truth.

Every man here knows that God's mercy toward David was not according to the law, but what that event teaches us is not what Paul teaches. Hananiah has already explained how that God made an exception concerning the Passover in Hezekiah's day and that He made an exception concerning the holy bread in David's time. But by no means did God intend those exceptions to become the rule, as Hananiah said. God even made an exception to the laws of nature when Joshua commanded the sun to stand still, and it did not move for the space of about a day.[193] But what fool would try to reconfigure our calendar to reflect in our everyday lives that exception? God abrogated the laws of nature again when He parted the Red Sea, dried its bed, and stood its waters up like a wall,[194] but does that mean we may walk across every sea on dry land whenever we will? Of course not! The exceptions are not meant to become the rule!

God has performed many miracles since the beginning of the world, but they are not miracles to Him, for nothing is difficult for Him. I doubt the word "miracle" is even used in heaven. We men consider the mighty works of God miracles because they are exceptions to the laws God has established in creation, and they are exceptions only because those laws remain in place. God has likewise established a law for man, the law of Moses. What Paul and Barnabas have done is invent a gospel based on exceptions instead of living in the law itself and marveling at His gracious exceptions.

Of course God is free to do as He will, whenever He will; no man denies that. He is God! But God has given us a law to keep, and men are fools who do not keep it. And they are the worst kind of fools who devise doctrines that excuse men from keeping it!

Council members: *Comments.*

Peter's Baptism of the Gentiles

Lamech: Answer a question for us, Paul.
Paul: I am here.

---

[193] Josh. 10:12–13.
[194] Ex. 14:16, 21–22.

Lamech: You hold that the Gentiles in Caesarea to whom Simon Peter went some years ago were made truly righteous only when they received the Spirit, for it brought a new kind of righteousness into their souls. Is that right?

Paul: The Spirit brought God's kind of righteousness into their souls, yes, and that is the only righteousness acceptable to God in this covenant.

Lamech: And after they received the Spirit, according to your gospel, God requires nothing of those Gentiles but to live upright lives, as the Spirit leads them?

Paul: Yes.

Lamech: I thought so. But that puzzles me. I have thought on it often since you confronted me with your gospel in Antioch. Feel free to correct me if I am wrong, but I believe that brother Simon baptized those Gentiles *after* they received the Spirit, contrary to your doctrine, brother.

Paul: That baptism made the Gentiles no purer in God's sight. Jesus' baptism had made their souls as clean as they could be.

Lamech: But what should we say to Cornelius, Paul, about brother Simon's decision to baptize him with John's baptism after Jesus had baptized him with the Spirit? Would you tell him that Simon had polluted with a dead ceremony what God had cleansed?

Paul: I would tell them the truth, that God had not at that time revealed my gospel and that brother Peter did as he felt best. I have no criticism of him at all for that.

Lamech: But how could we repair the damage – unbaptized them, if there is such a thing – so that they might be clean again?

Paul: Dead things such as water have no power either to cleanse or pollute the soul. That baptism did them no harm, and Peter commanded nothing else for them.

Matthew: Jesus said that only what comes out of a man defiles him, Lamech, not water. But I do think that you have raised a reasonable question. Simon, why did you baptize those Gentiles with water? I have never thought to ask that before now.

Simon Peter: What else was I to do? Jesus had given us no instructions for Gentiles. He didn't even forewarn us that he would baptize them with His Spirit, except in a vision which I understood only well enough to make me willing to go to that Gentile's house.

Lamech: But why baptize them? Why did you not command them to be circumcised instead? John's baptism was only for Israel. Why baptize the uncircumcised with our baptism? They did not even yet belong to our nation. To circumcise them, rather than to baptize them, was the proper order.

Simon Peter: I . . . I don't really know. I had no instructions. It seemed to be the right thing to do, since God had given them His Spirit. But I do understand why you question it.

Paul: I will explain to you why Peter baptized those Gentiles. Simon, may I?

Simon Peter: Yes, of course.

Paul: When God baptized the Gentiles with His Spirit, Peter knew they belonged to God, for God had then borne them witness, that they had believed and repented. And since they belonged to God, Peter baptized them because God had required John's baptism of His people since the day He sent John with it. God did not tell Peter to do that; Peter only assumed he should do it because it had always been required.

Lamech: God did not tell me to pray this morning, Paul, but I did. Did God have to tell Simon to do the thing that he already knew to do? Does God have to tell us everything, each day we live, in order for us to know what we should do?

Simon Peter: I learned from my experience at Cornelius' house that, yes, we must always be led by the Spirit to know what to do and what to say, and even what to think.

Paul: Knowing the law did not help Peter know what to do at Cornelius' house, Lamech. He went ahead with John's baptism because he thought he should, even though he knew that Jesus had already sanctified them. Peter was trying to figure it all out.

Simon Peter: I certainly was.

Paul Explains the Keys of the Kingdom of God

Paul: And if you recall, brothers, God had to force Peter to go to Caesarea in the first place because Peter did not understand the keys of the kingdom of God which Jesus had given him.[195]

Silas: And what do you say the keys of God's kingdom are, Paul?

Paul: When Jesus gave Peter the keys of the kingdom of heaven, what he was giving him was the authority to open the door of the kingdom of God to men, first to the Jews, next to the Samaritans, and lastly to the Gentiles. Peter used his first key, the key for the Jews, the day the Spirit first came, and when he used it, thousands of Jews believed and entered into the kingdom of God.

---

[195] Mt. 16:17–19.

Benjamin: But to the Samaritans, God sent Philip, not brother Simon.

Paul: Yes, but Philip could not open the door for them; he could only tell them about the kingdom. Tell us, Philip, when the Samaritans heard your preaching, and saw the miracles God worked through you, and repented, why did you not lay your hands on them to receive the Spirit?

Philip: I would have, but God would not allow it. The Samaritans were already circumcised, and I thought that since they had believed my preaching and repented, all I needed to do was to baptize them in water in the name of Jesus and they would receive the Spirit. But when I baptized them, the Spirit did not come.

Paul: And it did not come because their door was not yet open, and the door was not open because Peter, the man with the keys, was in Jerusalem.

Joseph: Yes, when word came to us that the Samaritans had received the word of God from Philip, the Spirit led us to send Simon, and John with him, expecting that the Samaritans would receive the Spirit.

Philip: Which they did, after Simon came and he and John laid their hands on them.

Paul: The only thing that those Samaritans had lacked was the man with the keys. They were circumcised; they had believed the gospel; they had repented; they had been baptized with John's baptism – and all of that was required of them, but they could not receive the Spirit because their door was not yet opened.

Simon Peter: Until I came?

Paul: Yes, Peter. You had to be there because the anointing to open the door of the kingdom was given to you, not Philip.

Barnabas: And in that instance, Simon, your anointing to open the door worked not through your mouth, the way it did the day the Spirit first came, but through your hands, when you laid your hands on the Samaritans and they received the Spirit.

Maschil: But after that, many other Samaritans received the Spirit without Simon being there. Does that mean he had only to open the door?

Paul: Yes. And since the day Peter opened that door, any Samaritan who believes, and repents, and is baptized in Jesus' name receives the Spirit.

Barnabas: And that is true of Jews, as well. Since Peter opened the Jews' door, any Jew may receive the Spirit, whether Simon is present or not. Both those doors are now open.

Simon Peter: But after that day in Samaria, there was one key remaining that I had not used, wasn't there?

Paul: Yes, Peter. You still held the key to the kingdom of God for the Gentiles.

Simon Peter: My God, I see it! That truly is what the Lord meant!

Paul: And when God forced you to go to those Gentiles, Peter, although you did not yet understand it and did not want to go, you went because you are a faithful servant of God.

Simon Peter: If I had known what the keys of the kingdom were, I would not have resisted going!

Paul: I know that; we all know that. And God knew it then. That is why He was patient with you, and why He interrupted you when you had said all that the Gentiles needed to hear. You had accomplished what God sent you to do, for the anointing that Jesus gave you unlocked the Gentiles' door when you obeyed God and preached to them. But Jesus did not anoint you to be the *teacher* of the Gentiles. That is my office.

Simon Peter: My Lord and my God! And I didn't even know what I was doing.

Paul: You didn't have to. God knew, and His love made up for your ignorance, and theirs.

Council members: *Comments.*

Kenaz: Brothers, I was in Joppa when Simon Peter came there and healed Dorcas, and I traveled with him to Caesarea when God sent him to Cornelius' house. To go there with Simon was not easy for me to do, as you certainly know, for we were forbidden by the custom of our fathers to enter into a Gentile's house. I can only speak for myself, but I feel sure that none of us who went with Simon would have gone, but for the vision that God gave him.

Council members: *Low conversation.*

Philip: Every man here would have felt the same way, especially since Jesus strictly forbade us to go to the Gentiles.

Elkanah: Yes, and we knew that. And none of us in Joppa knew why Jesus was sending Simon to Gentiles. The last thing we expected was that Jesus would baptize the heathen with the Spirit just because they believed Simon's message about Jesus.

Ahijah: That is so, but truthfully, I can't even say that it was the *last* thing I expected because I did not expect it at all!

Azariah: That's right, Ahijah. God receiving the heathen? It was unthinkable!

Ahijah: Impossible!

Eliezar: We were dumbfounded.

Kenaz: I don't think I slept for two days. I would lie in bed and ask myself, over and over, "What just happened? What did we just witness?"

Elkanah: Yes. "What has God done?"

Eliezar: That's it. We knew it was the work of God, but what did it mean?

Joel: It appears that God proved Solomon wrong about something, for Solomon once said, "There is no new thing under the sun."[196] But for God to grant Gentiles – uncircumcised Gentiles! – remission of sins was certainly a new thing. If we had not seen it for ourselves, I don't know that we could have believed it.

Elkanah: That's the truth.

Council members: *Comments.*

Barnabas: Simon, remind us of the warning God gave you before He sent you to Cornelius' house.

Simon Peter: The command He gave me in the vision I saw while on Simon the tanner's rooftop?

Barnabas: Yes, that one.

Simon Peter: Very well. In a stern voice, God said to me, "What I have cleansed, don't you call common!"

Barnabas: In other words, brothers, if God bore witness to those Gentiles, giving them the Spirit, then who is any man to condemn them? It is God that justifies, not us. Messiah Jesus is good, brothers, and he does good to those who are good.[197]

Benjamin: We are not saying that Jesus is not good, Brother Barnabas.

Barnabas: But you *are* saying that Jesus is not good *enough*, that he needs help from Moses to save men's souls.

Council members: *Comments.*

Hushai: Last year, Uzziel, Levi, and I stayed in Miletus five days, where our ship had put in for repairs, and I saw those pretentious philosophers – dogs, all of them! – gather in the agora every evening to debate vain issues, each one hoping to win the audience with a novel thought and be acclaimed as a new Anaxagoras. This convoluted conversation reminds me of that. Brothers, this doctrine is just another new thing, and it, too, will pass.

Paul: No, Hushai. This new thing is the new thing which God promised our fathers[198] and which He has accomplished in His Son, and it

---

[196] Eccl. 1:9.

[197] Ps. 125:4.

[198] Isa. 43:19.

will never pass away. Moreover, this new thing is not explained by your gospel, for your gospel still requires the old thing of the law. That is why those who went with Peter to Cornelius' house could not understand what God had done; none of the law's rites had been performed beforehand, which their gospel required; and so, to them, the Gentiles were still unfit for the Spirit. But God gave it anyway! And it is *my* gospel alone which explains why God did that.

Council members: *Comments.*

Hillel: The most effective deceiver is the man who is most thoroughly deceived. No false teacher is successful who is not first convinced of his own lies.

Nathan: Brothers, brothers! Perhaps this whole controversy is just a matter of emphasis, with Barnabas and Paul emphasizing the glory of Messiah more, and Hananiah and these men emphasizing the law more.

Micah: It is much more than that, Nathan. Even if Paul and Barnabas have learned some truth from God, one truth can be stressed to the neglect of an equally important truth, and when that is done, the beauty of the whole is marred. What God has done in Israel is a beautiful thing, and He has crowned our history now with Messiah Jesus, perfecting His work forever.

PART 3
PAUL DECLARES THAT MOSES' LAW WILL END

—❊—

The Jews Will Have To Change

Joseph: Paul, my fiery son, there is an old saying, "The ear tries speech as the palate tastes food."[199] And I remember a parable Jesus once told us about new wine tasting unpleasant to those accustomed to aged wine. These new things are not easy to swallow for those who have feasted their whole lives on ancient truth.

Perhaps you should let these brothers hear your answer to this question, for it is in their hearts, though none of them have expressed it in this manner: if the Spirit was given so that all who believe, both Jew and Gentile, might "serve God in one accord", as the prophet said,[200] and if Jesus prayed fervently for all believers to be as one, how can unity ever be realized if we Jews are pleasing God by worshipping according to the law and the Gentiles who believe are also pleasing God by *not* worshipping according to the law?

Micah: Yes, Paul – and thank you, brother Joseph. That question *is* in my heart. If both are pleasing God, how can either ever cease worshipping the way they do now? If there are two true gospels – and I am not saying that is the case – how will the difference ever be resolved?

Paul: The difference will not last, Micah. It will be this way only for a season.

Micah: What do you mean, "for a season"? If what you say is true, Paul, then someone, at some point, will have to change if we are to be united. Whom will God command to change at the close of this "season"? We Jews or the heathen who believe?

Paul: We Jews.

Council members: *Talking loudly among themselves.*

Paul: God loves and is very gentle with His people, brothers. Having commanded us Jews to keep the law, He does not now command us to violate our conscience and stop keeping it. But in time, we will be required to grow in grace and understand that the law's purpose has been fulfilled.

---

[199] Job 34:3.
[200] Zeph. 3:9.

Hushai: We know that God spoke through Moses and the prophets, and through Jesus, but we do not know where you have gotten the things you say, Paul. What prophet ever said, "No law! No circumcision! No sacrifice! No Sabbath!" Jesus told us that he was the Lord of the Sabbath,[201] but you would do away with the Sabbath and make him Lord of nothing.

Council members: *Comments, pro and con.*

Hillel: Men and brothers, as God lives! Can you not see what is happening? First, Paul and Barnabas argue that the Gentiles will do wrong by keeping the law, and now, when they see that most of you agree with that error, they are emboldened to state their true purpose – to cause *Israel* to cease from it! Uzziel warned you of what these men were up to! Who cannot now see it?

Council members: *Comments, pro and con.*

Nahum Reminds Paul of Stephen's Execution

Nahum: Paul, my son, allow me.

Paul: Of course, sir.

Nahum: I was standing by the south gate when the rulers and men of the city dragged young Stephen out, past me. It was a terrible sight! When I asked someone what was happening, the man told me they were taking Stephen out to the valley to stone him. I asked him why, and he said that Stephen had spoken blasphemous things against Moses and God.

Maschil: What things, brother Nahum?

Nahum: He told me that several witnesses had testified they heard Stephen saying that Jesus would destroy Jerusalem and change the customs that Moses commanded.[202] So, you must beware, Paul, where you speak these things. Outside this room, in the streets of this city, your words would provoke murderous wrath.

Jacobus: That is certainly true, Nahum. But there is no danger here among us of such evil being done to a righteous man.

Council members: *Amen. Etc.*

Jacobus: Speak freely, Paul, and all of you.

Paul: I was present at Stephen's trial, brothers. I heard his testimony, and I was as blind as anyone to the truth he spoke. I know how wrong God's truth can sound until God opens our ears. I was glad when the rulers dragged Stephen out of the city. And I was glad when the stones

---

[201] Mt. 12:8.

[202] Acts 6:11–14.

began to beat out his life. Would to God I had been in *his* place instead of the place I was in! But now, I stand here among brothers whom I am not even worthy to be among, and I am confessing to you the truth for which Stephen died!

Lamech: Stephen died for confessing the truth; that is true. But what was the truth that Stephen confessed? He did *not* confess that our customs would change; that is only what the false witnesses accused him of saying.

Brother Nahum, the mob passed me, too, dragging Stephen out. It was indeed a gruesome sight. And I, too, questioned men who had been there and heard what Stephen said. What I learned was that the Sanhedrin did not condemn Stephen because of what the false witnesses said but for what Stephen himself said. He told the judges that they were stiff-necked and uncircumcised and that they had not kept the law God gave them. That's the point at which they began reviling him. They were hypocrites, and Stephen exposed them. Then Stephen – who kept the law – suddenly cried out that he saw Messiah Jesus – who also kept the law – standing at the right hand of God – who gave the law – and those wicked men who were not keeping the law dragged Stephen out of the city and stoned him.[203] But now, men and brothers, Paul would have us to believe that not keeping the law will soon be a righteous thing. So, Paul, how can you say that Stephen died for the gospel you preach?

Paul: Since the beginning of the world, the Spirit has been declaring my gospel through righteous men, though they did not understand it. And they were hated and persecuted by wicked men who also did not understand it.

Council members: *Comments.*

Paul: I was there at Stephen's trial, Lamech, and I heard him for myself. Fools consider it a crime to speak the truth, and Stephen spoke truth to a chamber full of fools that day.

Council members: *Amen. Etc.*

Paul: What he told those wicked judges is not that they were uncircumcised, as you were apparently told, but that they were uncircumcised *in heart*. And when he told them they were not keeping the law, he meant that they were not keeping it *in heart*. And as for the accusation against Stephen, that he prophesied that Jesus will change the customs of Moses, that accusation may not have been a false one, for the Spirit could have moved Stephen to speak of my gospel. I don't know if God did that, but I do know Stephen was a prophet, and the Spirit moved the prophets often to speak of my gospel. And so, those false witnesses may have been testi-

---

[203] Acts 7:51–58.

fying of something Stephen actually had said in the Spirit. Did not the false witnesses who testified against Jesus at his trial repeat things he actually had said, though they twisted his words to accomplish an evil purpose?[204]

Council members: *Comments.*

Paul: I heard Stephen when he reminded the judges of Solomon's prayer to God at the dedication of the temple: "Behold, heaven cannot contain you! How much less this house that I have built?"[205] Stephen was very bold to declare before the Sanhedrin that God does not dwell in temples made by hands. He was risking his life when he reminded them of Isaiah's words: "Heaven is my throne, and the earth, my footstool. Where is this house that *you* would build for me?"[206] God's temple is in heaven, brothers, just as the prophets said,[207] and by the Spirit, we have access into that temple, where our God is.

Council members: *Comments.*

Arguments Concerning the Law Ending

Hananiah: But brother Paul, the righteous in Israel have always had access to God in heaven. Did not David say, "The eyes of the LORD are upon the righteous, and His ears are open to their cry"?[208] And did not the LORD say to Moses in the mountain, "I have surely seen the affliction of my people who are in Egypt, and I have heard their cry"?[209]

Paul: Yes, God heard us, and yes, God blessed us, but only on the condition that His Son would come and pay the price for it all. Everything depended on Jesus, for we had no inner connection, no fellowship with the heart and mind of God.

Under the law, there was atonement made for sin, and once those rites were observed, God extended forgiveness to the transgressors. But none of the sins forgiven under the law were blotted out of God's book in heaven until the blood of His Son was shed for them; the blood of goats and oxen can never take away man's sins.

Council members: *Comments.*

Micah: As often as the prophets spoke of Messiah, surely, if what you and Barnabas say is true, they would have said it, too. But they did not.

---

204 Mt. 26:59–61.

205 1Kgs. 8:27.

206 Isa. 66:1–2a; Acts 7:49–50.

207 E.g., Ps. 11:4; Mic. 1:2.

208 Ps. 34:15.

209 Ex. 3:7.

Cleopas: We all say things now that the prophets did not say, Micah, because we know the Son, and the prophets did not know him.

Micah: But even if we lay aside everything said in the law and the prophets, we still have the righteous example of Jesus himself, who walked uprightly according to the law and said, "*You* will stay in my love if *you* keep my commandments, just as I have kept my Father's commandments and stay in His love."[210] I want us to stay in the Father's love, Paul. You would lead us into His wrath!

Eli, Hushai, Nadab, Hillel, Lamech, Hilkiah: *Amen. That's right, Micah! Ect.*

Micah: One day, as we were traveling with Jesus, he met ten lepers who wanted to be healed. Jesus did not heal them right then, as he had done many others, but commanded them to go to the priests to offer the sacrifices that Moses' law required for those healed of leprosy.[211] And it was only when they obeyed him, only after they had left us and were on their way to the priests, that they were healed. Why would Jesus have commanded them to obey the law if God had sent him here to do away with the law?

Barnabas: God has often commanded His servants to do things which they later ceased from doing when God's purpose was accomplished. God commanded Moses to build a tent for His service in the wilderness, but later, God gave David the design for a temple to replace Moses' tent.

Hananiah: But that dealt only with the *location* of worship, Barnabas. God's law continued to be observed in Solomon's temple even though Moses' tabernacle was put away. Moses' sanctuary had to be a tent because the people were constantly moving, traveling with it from Egypt to this land. But once we were established in the land, God chose one place for His service, as He had promised, saying to Moses, "When *you* have settled in the land, there will be a place which the LORD *your* God will choose as a dwelling place for His name."[212] So, while God may give a new commandment for a specific situation, God commanded His law to be kept everywhere, whether in Moses' tent or in Solomon's temple, whether out in the wilderness or in Jerusalem, or anywhere else.

Barnabas: I see how you are looking at that, Hananiah, but . . .

Simeon: Whatever God commands stands forever, brothers.

Barnabas: . . . unless He gives a new commandment that differs from a previous one.   What happened to the man who refused to obey the

---

[210] Jn. 15:10.

[211] Lk. 17:12–14.

[212] Dt. 12:10–11.

prophet when he commanded that man by the word of the LORD to strike him? Everyone in Israel knew that God strictly forbade anyone to harm His servants, for God had commanded through David a hundred years before, "Do not touch my anointed ones, and do not harm my prophets!"[213] And so, when God sent the prophet to that man, saying, "Strike me!" he would not strike him, for God had said not to. He obeyed God's old commandment, and God killed him for doing so.[214]

Council members: *Comments*.

Barnabas: And you know what God did to Moses at Kadesh-barnea when Moses obeyed God's old commandment to strike a rock[215] instead of obeying His new commandment to speak to a rock.[216] That error cost Moses dearly.[217]

Jared: Yes, Barnabas, but those were minor commands that applied to specific times and places. Striking a prophet or a rock is not to be compared with the eternal covenant of God. What is a grain of sand to a mountain?

Barnabas: I was responding to the comment that "whatever God commands stands forever." That is manifestly not always the case. Whatever God says now is what we must do, brother Jared. As brother Daniel said, "The only truth that exists is what God is saying today."

Andrew: And speaking of major commandments instead of minor ones, brother Jared, God commanded Israel not to drink any manner of blood, and that was no small thing. To break that commandment would cost a man his soul, for God said, "If any man of the house of Israel consumes any kind of blood, I will cut him off from among his people.[218] And this: "*You* shall not consume any blood, whether of bird or beast. Any soul who consumes any blood, that soul shall also be cut off from his people."[219]

Lamech: I know where you are going with this.

Andrew: You should. You were there with us the day Jesus said that the only way to have eternal life is to drink his blood.[220] So, how can you

---

213 Ps. 105:15.

214 1Kgs. 20:35–36.

215 Ex. 17:6.

216 Num. 20:8.

217 Num. 20:12.

218 Lev. 17:10.

219 Lev. 7:26–27.

220 Jn. 6:53–56.

think Moses' law will continue forever when Jesus said such a change as that was coming?

Council members: *Comments.*

Andrew: Brothers, God has commandments yet to give us which may sound as strange to our ears as that one from Jesus did, and who knows what we will be called upon to do?

Lamech: You men are just engaging in intellectual gymnastics. Jesus was speaking only of eating and drinking spiritually, Andrew, and many left him that day and never came back.[221] He was not saying what you are saying, that Israel must cease from the law. That is unthinkable! And that is also not a small matter, Andrew, a mere afterthought which God just happened never to mention in the prophets.

Council members: *Comments.*

Barnabas: But He did, Lamech! What we are telling you *is* in the prophets.

Eli: We have not imagined that God said, "Cursed be the man who does not obey the words of this covenant" and "Cursed be anyone who does not confirm the commandments of this law by doing them."[222] God really said those things, and He commanded all Israel to say amen when they heard those words, Paul.[223] Do you and Barnabas say amen to the word of God?

Hushai: I say amen to it!

Nadab, Hillel, Lamech, Hilkiah: *Amen! We do! Yes! Etc.*

Paul: Far be it from me to say to any Jew that he should forsake the law, as long as it pleases God for the Jews to keep it. I believe God will certainly curse whoever among us would dare forsake it; indeed, every man who is circumcised must keep the law, every element of it, just as it is written. I myself keep the commandments, and I have done so from my youth.[224]

Eli: But you admit that your aim is to have us to cease from it! Be honest, Paul!

Paul: It is not my "aim"; it is the purpose of God.

Eli: David said, "Rivers of waters run down my eyes because they do not keep your law,"[225] but you and Barnabas would weep for those who *do* keep it! Brother Jacobus! John! Simon! Be sensible. You are good,

---

[221] Jn. 6:66.

[222] Dt. 27:26a.

[223] Dt. 27:26b.

[224] Acts 26:4–5.

[225] Ps. 119:136.

godly men. Do you truly believe that the law will die which nurtured us in righteousness?

John: I believe the law was dead to start with, Eli, and we were dead with it, and I believe that Messiah brought us life, just as he said: "I am come that they might have life, and have it abundantly."[226]

Jacobus: "Die" is just a term, Eli. The point is that something greater than the law has come, and Paul's message is that the "something" that is greater than the law is Jesus and that he is so much greater than the law that he alone does for our souls all that God now requires.

Council members: *Comments.*

Eli: I understand what Paul is saying, Jacobus, but it is only what Paul says, not what God has ever said.

Simon Peter: Brother Eli, be slow to judge these things; Paul says things that are hard to understand, I know, but he has received something from God that we need to hear.

Barnabas: And I emphasize again, brothers, that Paul and I acknowledge and respect the gospel you preach, as long as you preach it to the Jews. And we will preach our gospel to the Gentiles. Paul and I have said we know that God is pleased that we Jews keep the law at this time. But the one of whom the law spoke has come, and a new and living way of worship is taking the place of the old one.

Paul: We can all agree, brothers, that every god that men worship that is not the One whom Jesus revealed is false, no matter what men think.

Council members: *Comments.*

Paul: But it is equally true that no matter what men think, every *way* that men worship is false if it is not the way that Jesus made possible by sending us the Spirit!

Council members: *Comments.*

Benjamin Begins To See

Benjamin: Brother Paul, God told Moses that the high priest was to "light the lamps at twilight and burn it as a continual incense before the LORD *throughout your generations.*"[227]   And God told Moses that the children of Israel were "to observe the Sabbath throughout their generations as a covenant *forever.*"[228]   How can you say that we, not the Gentiles, will have to change?

---

[226] Jn. 10:10.

[227] Ex. 30:8.

[228] Ex. 31:16.

Paul: [*slowly, discerning something*] Do you think Barnabas and I contrived all this, Benjamin? Do you think our gospel was *not* given to us by Jesus?

Benjamin: [*hesitates*] Well, I . . . What I think is irrelevant, brother Paul. What you think is irrelevant, too. What any man thinks is irrelevant. Can't you see what Uzziel said, that we must judge all things by the measure which we know came from God, the truth spoken by Moses and the prophets?

Paul: Is that all that has come to us from God, Benjamin? Hasn't His Spirit also now come from God, and doesn't the Spirit of God give us wisdom that is beyond Moses and the prophets?

Council members: *Comments.*

Paul: Jesus has liberated us from having to make judgments based on our understanding of handwritten material. Listen to what the Spirit is saying to you, Benjamin. The Spirit is bearing witness to your heart right now to the truth. The Lord is talking to you, Benjamin. Believe him.

Lamech: Such psychological tricks may work among the Gentiles, Paul, but they won't work here.

Paul: It is no trick, Lamech. Jesus is showing the truth to Benjamin; I can see it. And he will soon be free from reliance upon things he can see, and he will learn to look rather to what cannot be seen. That is the faith of Abraham, who looked to the invisible God. Everything that can be seen will pass away, but that which cannot be seen is eternal.

Philip: Amen, Paul. Jesus commanded us to judge by the Spirit, and not to judge by what we see or what we hear.[229]

Nadab: And you think that includes the law?

Paul: Can you see it?

Nadab: I can see you; does that mean you are dead and gone?

Paul: Yes, it does. What you see of me, my fleshly body, and what I see of you, *is* dead – dead to the things of God – and it will soon be altogether gone, just as the law soon will be.

Council members: *Comments.*

The Old and the New

Paul: Believe me, men and brothers! God will soon call upon us Jews to cease altogether from the law and to trust in Jesus alone. We may then,

---

[229] Jn. 7:24.

at last, be of one faith with the Gentiles, walking together in the law of the Spirit, and there will be one fold and one Shepherd.[230]

Hushai: There is already one fold – Israel! – and the uncircumcised are not in it! And there is already one shepherd – Jesus! He is Lord over us all, Jew and Gentile alike, and we must serve him alike – in the law that he obeyed! Brothers, we do not diminish the value of the Spirit or the price that was paid for it. We know that the Spirit is God's testimony of His Son, and we praise Him for it, just as you do.

Barnabas: Oh, but you do diminish the value of the Spirit when you add something to it.

Hushai: But how have *we* added the law to the Spirit? You yourself admit that God added the Spirit to the law! The law came first, not second.

Council members: *Comments.*

Barnabas: The law had to be first because it was a testimony that God's Son was coming; but now, the Spirit has been given as a testimony that he came. You are trying to add to that new testimony the old one that has been fulfilled. What need have we of a testimony that Messiah is coming? He has already come! What men need now is God's witness that Messiah was here and that he is coming again!

Micah: I just don't see it, Barnabas. Men need both God's law and God's confirmation of it. That is what God has commanded: look to both the law and the Spirit! Yes, men must receive God's testimony of His Son, and we do not condemn the Gentiles who have received it. But God said to tell men to look to both the Spirit and the law, not just to the Spirit alone.

Maschil: Every man here thanks God for giving us such a sure testimony of His Son as the Spirit. But it is impossible to believe that God's pouring out of the Spirit requires that we should cease from His other witness, the law. It seems more reasonable to me to say that God sent His witness of the Spirit to *assure* the observance of the law, not to end it. Brother Barnabas, I have always esteemed you as my elder, but you are talking riddles to me.

Council members: *Comments.*

Lamech: If the doctrine taught by Barnabas and Paul had truly been God's plan all along, as they say, then surely, Jesus would have prepared us better for it. When did Jesus tell us that circumcision would be no more, that the feasts would cease being observed, or that the Sabbaths

---

[230] Jn. 10:16.

would no longer be kept? No, my brothers, if Jesus had anticipated this doctrine, he would have told us that it was coming.

John: But Jesus did suggest such things, Lamech. We just could not understand him.

Philip: And it was a good thing that we did not understand him, for if we had, it would have been too much for us. He even said so the night before he died.[231]

Hushai: But haven't we all learned very much since the Spirit came? Jesus was not referring to the things Barnabas and Paul teach when he said he had other truths to teach us.

Matthew: Don't speak too soon, Hushai. God does all things according to His own will, and whenever His will changes, we must change with it.

Micah: If God changes, we certainly must change with Him, Matthew, but we must first be sure that God has made a change.

Council members: *That is true. Yes. Etc.*

Micah: But a change like this is more than I can see God making. God's ways are straightforward and clear; this new doctrine seems convoluted to me. It stirs up strife and debate.

Nadab: The truth cannot be simpler. We are to keep the commandments of God. That is as fundamental to righteousness as can be.

Maschil: Amen! The meaning of what God said to our fathers could not have been more clear when He said that the law is "an everlasting covenant" and that only the wicked do not keep it.[232] How much clearer could He be?

Council members: *Comments.*

Micah: And what would make God's everlasting law "everlasting", but that it is to be everlastingly kept by His people? It seems unreasonable to think that the coming of the Spirit would bring an end to the law, when God Himself called the law an "everlasting covenant".

Barnabas: Righteous men of old did say that the law is everlasting;[233] however, God later spoke of another covenant, saying in Jeremiah, "I will make a new covenant with the house of Israel and with the house of Judah, not like the covenant that I made with their fathers in the day I took them out of the land of Egypt. For this is the covenant that I will make

---

[231] Jn. 16:12.

[232] Isa. 24:5, et. al.

[233] E.g., David, in 1Chronicles 16:17 (cf. Ps. 105:10).

with the house of Israel after those days, says the LORD: I will put my law within them and write it on their heart."[234]

Hillel: Your handling of the scriptures does not hold up to scrutiny, Barnabas. It may sound good and right to some men, but what you are saying is neither good nor right.

Council members: *Comments.*

Jacobus: What do you mean, Hillel?

Hillel: Did you not hear the prophecy, Jacobus? Did any of you hear it? What did Barnabas himself just tell us that Jeremiah said about this new covenant? He said, "I will make a new covenant *with the house of Israel.*" God said nothing at all about making a covenant with Gentiles. There is one fold, Israel, and one shepherd, Jesus the son of David, as Ezekiel said, "I have exalted one shepherd to be over them, and he will feed them."[235]

Council members: *Comments.*

Hillel: God spoke through Moses and described this land, the land of Canaan, as the land of rest for Israel, did He not, Barnabas?[236]

Barnabas: Yes.

Hillel: But after our fathers had dwelt here for many generations, God warned the righteous through the prophet Micah, saying, "Rise up and leave, for this is not your rest! It is polluted."[237] And about that same time, God promised yet another rest, the holy Spirit, which we have now received. For Isaiah said, "He will speak to this people with stammering lips and another tongue, to whom He said, 'This is the rest with which you will cause the weary one to rest,' and, 'This is the refreshing.'"[238]

Nadab: But was not Isaiah prophesying of the foreigners that God sent to chasten our nation?

Hillel: Yes, but God used ancient events as parables for what He would do at a later time.

Nadab: That is true.

Simeon: Yes, that is true. That is true. He is the God of all the earth; He shapes and uses nations as He will.

Nadab: But why would He call this land our rest if it really was not?

Lamech: Because it *is* our rest, Nadab.

Nadab: Oh.

---

[234] Jer. 31:31–33.

[235] Ezek. 34:23.

[236] Dt. 12:9.

[237] Mic. 2:10.

[238] Isa. 28:11–12.

Lamech: God only *added* the rest of His Spirit to it. Men and brothers, this land has provided our people great rest and safety from our enemies, just as God promised. And even though God has added to us this precious rest of the Spirit, the land is still here, is it not?

Council members: *Comments.*

Lamech: And by the mercies of God, we are still in it, are we not?

Council members: *Comments.*

Lamech: So, tell me, brothers. Has this land of rest been *replaced* by the spiritual rest Jesus purchased for us, or has a sweet rest only been added to the rest God already gave us?

Eli, Hilkiah, Hushai, Hillel, Nadab: *Added to it! Etc.*

Lamech: Yes, it has been added to that rest, and it is wrong not to think so.

Hillel: And that is not all the safety that this land has provided us, Lamech. Being given our own land not only provides us with safety from foreign enemies, but safety also from enemies within our borders. For God said, "In the Assembly, there shall be one ordinance for *you* and for the foreigner who dwells among you, an ordinance forever throughout *your* generations. There shall be one law and one custom for *you* and for the foreigner who dwells with *you*."[239] So then, having both the law and the land enables us to govern the land according to God's law, to condemn transgressors and to rid ourselves of them. This is what God commanded! And by enforcing the law in this land, God said, "You shall purge the evil from your midst, and all Israel shall hear of it, and fear."[240] The prophets said nothing about our land being a mere symbol of the spiritual rest which Jesus brought us. No, brothers. We do not discard what God said yesterday just because He says something more today.

Council members: *Comments.*

Hillel: Consider what I say, brothers, for it is indisputable truth. In ancient time, God made a covenant with Noah and with his sons, that He would never again destroy the earth with a flood. And He sealed that covenant with a rainbow, saying, "This is the sign of the covenant which I am making between me and you and every living soul that is with you, unto all generations."[241] Then, many years later, when God made a covenant of circumcision with father Abraham,[242] did that new covenant do away with the covenant God had previously made with Noah?

---

[239] Num. 15:15–16.

[240] Dt. 21:21b.

[241] Gen. 9:8–13.

[242] Gen. 17:9–11.

Council members: *Comments.*

Hillel: Do we not still see God's rainbow in the sky, assuring us of His continued commitment to the covenant He made with Noah?

Council members: *Comments.*

Hillel: Yes, your own eyes have seen God's rainbow in the heavens, testifying that God keeps His covenants and that a new covenant does not void older ones.

Lamech: Amen, Hillel!

Council members: *Comments.*

Lamech: Now, brothers, we all give thanks to God for the atoning work of Messiah Jesus. But these men say that the atoning work of him who kept the law does not lead other men to keep it. No, brothers! Jesus suffered and died to confirm the law so that all men everywhere would know that the law is of God and would obey it. Didn't Jesus warn us not to think he had come to do away with the law, but to fulfill it? We heard him with our own ears say, "Do not think I have come to destroy the law or the prophets. I did not come to destroy, but to fulfill."[243]

Council members: *Comments.*

Lamech: Moreover, the addition of the Spirit to our worship is not the only addition that God has ever made to our worship. You said earlier, Paul, that God gave David a revelation concerning how to build the temple, and that is true. And in that revelation, God expanded our praise in music and instituted the order of priestly service that is practiced to this day.[244] But when God made that great change, that new addition to our faith, no one took David's revelation to mean that God's revelations to Noah, or Abraham, or Moses were thereby voided. None of the changes God made to our worship through the centuries did away with the law; they only made the law more perfect. This is what Jesus meant when he said he had come to fulfill the law. He made our worship as perfect as it can be when he sent us the Spirit to perfect us who were keeping the law.

This is precisely what God promised that Messiah would do, saying in Ezekiel, "I will put a new spirit within them so that they may walk in my statutes, and keep my judgments, and do them."[245] Listen to those words, men and brothers! God said the very reason for giving men His Spirit is to empower them to keep His law!

Simeon: Oh, that is so good, Lamech! Amen. Jesus baptized us with the Spirit to give us power for service.

---

[243] Mt. 5:17.
[244] 1Chron. 23:5; 28:11–19; 2Chron. 7:6.
[245] Ezek. 11:19–20.

Hananiah: And in that same place in Ezekiel, God promised that He would give us something else when He sent the Spirit. He said, "I will give them one heart," and that is a blessing not to be held in light esteem, brothers. I remind you, yet again, that God's people were enjoying perfect unity before this troublesome doctrine arose! We were all serving God together with one heart and soul. But now, look! Our sweet harmony has been destroyed!

Council members: *Comments.*

John: Our harmony will not change, Hananiah, if we but acknowledge one another's calling. Jesus has sent Paul and Barnabas to the Gentiles; leave them to their task, and we will continue to minister to Israel. We did not send you men to Antioch as we had sent Barnabas. You went on your own, and you erred by teaching those Gentiles that they must obey Moses' law. That message is true only among us, and it remains true only so long as it remains among us.

Hillel: It is incomprehensible to me, John, as close to the Lord Jesus as you once were, that you would say such a thing. A child could see the error of this new doctrine! Watch this now, and I will show you how foolish it is. Brother Nicodemus, may I ask you about your private visit with Messiah?

Nicodemus: Certainly.

Hillel: Did Jesus not tell you that we all must be born again?

Nicodemus: Yes, he did.

Hillel: Well, sir. What happened? Did something go wrong?

Nicodemus: I do not follow you.

Hillel: You heard Barnabas say, in so many words, that Messiah's new covenant is replacing the first one, did you not?

Nicodemus: Yes.

Hillel: Then, why did your new birth not replace your first one?

Nicodemus: What do you mean?

Hillel: You were born of God when you were baptized with the Spirit in that upper room. Is that not so?

Nicodemus: Yes, of course.

Hillel: But you still have the hands that your first birth gave you. Why were they not replaced when you were born again? Why do you still eat and drink the fruits of the fields? Why has God not replaced that first body of yours with a new body?

Nicodemus: I believe that He will, in time.

Hillel: So do I, sir. So do I – but *in the resurrection,* not here in this life. Your first birth with its fleshly body is still here, just as the law is still here. Isn't that true?

Nicodemus: [*slowly*] I suppose so, yes.

Hillel: Thank you, sir. Barnabas, do you now see? The new covenant God has made did not replace the covenant God made with Israel at Mount Sinai any more than our new birth replaced our first one; it was only added to it, fulfilling it and making it perfect. The coming of the Spirit confirmed, first of all, that the law is of God, and secondly, that the righteous are those who keep it. You have already been reminded that every soul on whom the Spirit fell when it first came was keeping the law, and it has been that way since, except for the ignorant Gentiles, *who should be taught better!*

Hilkiah: It seems to me that the truth is proved by every measure given to us. God's will is clearly that all men keep His law and believe in His Son. That truth is based upon the unmovable rock of Scripture, and it is as plain to me as truth can be.

Eli, Lamech, Hushai, Hillel, Nadab: *Amen! That's right, Hilkiah. Etc.*

Hushai: We are not insensible to your arguments, Barnabas. We are reasonable men. But one can see why your message appeals to the heathen and not to the chosen people of God.

Paul: It is not meant to appeal to the Jews because it was not given to me for them.

Hushai: But what are we to believe, Paul, when so many scriptures contradict you and Barnabas, or when you say illogical things that have never been heard in Israel?

Paul: I cannot make you see; that is God's place. I can only testify to the revelation that Jesus has given me.

Eli: And we can only wait for you to tell us which prophet or wise man said that the entrance of one covenant means the end of the previous one.

Logic

Daniel: My friends, logic is a sharp and useful tool; I wish more people were skilled in its use. However, logic is useful only in matters pertaining to this life. In the kingdom of God, revelation is logic, and faith provides us the skill to use it. Some of you will remember how miserably our own logic failed us when we were trying to understand and follow Jesus before the Spirit came.

Apostles: *Oh yes. We certainly do. Etc.*

Daniel: Did it seem logical to any of us that Messiah should be abused and die?

Council members: *Comments.*

Silas: No, it did not. We found it so illogical that, when he died, we gave up hope that Jesus was our Messiah.

Daniel: Who among us went to Jesus' tomb on the third day to see him rise from the dead?

Andrew: Nobody.   Not one of us believed he would rise from the dead.

Cleopas: You all know what Salmon and I did on the third day.[246] We bade you farewell and left town, certain that it was all over. Oh, we still believed that Jesus had been a great prophet, to be sure, the greatest prophet ever. But Messiah? That was impossible. He was dead.

Philip: That's how it was for all of us. Jesus told us he would meet us in Galilee after he rose from the dead, but after his crucifixion, none of us went to Galilee to meet him. We didn't believe Jesus would be there because, well, because he was dead.

Simon Peter: We never understood what Jesus meant by "rise from the dead"[247] because he was Israel's Messiah, and the prophets said Messiah would live forever. So, what did Jesus mean when he said he would rise from the dead? We just couldn't figure it out. And when he died, that ended all our hope in him as Israel's Messiah.

Cleopas: We didn't even believe the women on the third day when they rushed in, saying they had seen Jesus alive again. I assumed they had only seen a vision in their excitement,[248] and Salmon and I went on and left town.

Andrew: And later that day, Cleopas, the rest of us didn't believe you and Salmon when you returned and told us that you had seen Jesus, too.

Cleopas: But I understood why you didn't believe. After all, we had not believed the women. We just could not take it in, that a tortured and crucified man could be the unconquerable Messiah who would destroy the wicked and reign forever over the whole world. We were all utterly dejected, and afraid. It was all so completely illogical.

Daniel: So, my brothers, you see that logic cannot lead us in the realm of the Spirit. Revelation alone keeps the children of God on the right path,

---

[246] The actual name of Cleopas' companion that day is not revealed in Scripture. Their story is found in Luke 24:13–35.

[247] Mk. 9:9–10.

[248] Lk. 24:23.

as Solomon said, "Where there is no vision, the people are unrestrained."[249]

Nahum: That is certainly true, Daniel. Whenever there was no vision in Israel, as in the days when the prophet Samuel was a boy,[250] matters went poorly for us, for everyone went his own way. Nevertheless, the objections which have been raised should be answered, for many in our nation will ask such things.

Daniel: Agreed.

Barnabas and Paul Respond to Arguments against the Law Ending

Nahum: Barnabas, or Paul, what do you say to the objections of these brothers?

Barnabas: Jesus said that heaven and earth will pass away.[251] Then, if this land is our rest, as Lamech has said, where will our rest be when God destroys heaven and earth?

Hananiah: It will be with Messiah, wherever that may be.

Council members: *Comments.*

Hillel: Besides that, Barnabas, the future is not the point. Jesus said that as long as heaven and earth endure, "not one iota or serif of the law will pass away until all things have come to pass."[252] So, the real question is, why do you and Paul teach that the law will pass away before heaven and earth are destroyed, when Jesus said it would not? Whatever happens after they are destroyed is not our concern.

Nathan: Amen. As long as heaven and earth stand, not one iota of the law will be done away with, just as Jesus said.

Barnabas: It is true that our earthly future is not the point, Hillel; how can there even be an earthly future if earth is to be destroyed? But eternity certainly *is* the point because that is where our rest must be if God does away with this world. So, my question remains, where will your rest be when heaven and earth are destroyed? If your rest is the Spirit of God, you will be safe forever, but if you put your hope in a carnal thing such as this land, you will be destroyed with it.

Council members: *Comments.*

Paul: How can anything of this world be eternal if everything in this world will pass away. Messiah's new covenant is eternal because it is

---

[249] Prov. 29:18a.

[250] 1Sam. 3:1.

[251] Mt. 24:35.

[252] Mt. 5:18.

spiritual. Moses' law cannot be eternal because it is in the flesh, requiring earthly elements such as water, fire, incense, gold and silver, and so forth. Therefore, the law and its works will certainly perish with the earth. The eternal law of God's Spirit, written on our hearts, has replaced the temporal law with its earthly commandments!

Council members: *Comments.*

Hushai: But where are your scriptures, Paul? You sound like an Athenian philosopher! Logic may be of little worth when reasoning about divine things, but philosophy is worth even less. By your philosophy, when Messiah gives us to drink of living water from heaven, we should stop drinking water from our wells because that kind of water is "in the flesh". It just doesn't hold up, Paul.

Council members: *Comments.*

Barnabas: Brothers, please! Jesus has given us something good for His children, not something evil!

Jared: Is it good, Barnabas, that Moses said the law "is not a vain thing for you"[253] when you and Paul say that the law *is* a vain thing, or at least soon will be? Moses commanded Israel to "apply *your* hearts to all the words of this law. For it is *your life*."[254]

Paul: The Spirit is life, brother Jared; the law is lifeless.

Hilkiah: If the Spirit is life, then when it writes the law on our hearts, it makes the law alive in us.

Paul: Not so. It makes *us* alive, and when we come alive to God, we see that the law is a dead, carnal thing. God's law is a living, spiritual law!

Jared: God's law has *always* been spiritual.

Paul: Yes, but *we* have *never* been spiritual. We never had anything but our carnal nature with which to serve God before Messiah brought us God's life.

Hilkiah: But we had God's law.

Paul: . . . which was dead.

Hilkiah: It was dead, and yet it promised life to all who kept it? God said, "*You* must keep my statutes and my judgments, for the man who does them shall also live by them.[255]

Paul: Those who lived under the law will be judged by the law, and if they have been faithful to the law, then they *will* live forever. God was

---

[253] Dt. 32:47a.
[254] Dt. 32:46a, 47b.
[255] Lev. 18:5.

not speaking of those who will be judged by the perfect law of liberty from the carnal law.

Barnabas: Brothers, who can think that a *living* God intended for man to perform *lifeless* works forever?

Eli: We do!

Hilkiah, Lamech, Hushai, Hillel, Nadab: *Amen! That's right, Eli. Etc.*

Eli: Dozens of times in the law, God said He had given us statutes that would continue forever.[256] How many scriptures will it take to persuade you to believe what is irrefutably the word of God instead of clinging to whatever else you think you heard from Jesus?

The works of the law are lifeless only if men do not put life into them! *Not* keeping them is what makes them dead, Barnabas! When we perform the holy rites, they live! You and Paul are the ones who would kill the law, not God.

Paul: How can we kill what was never alive? And if we give our lives to dead things, they will kill us, for David said of idols, "Those who make them become like them, as well as everyone who trusts in them."[257]

Nadab: Do you make God's holy law equal to idols?

Paul: Of course not. The law is holy; we know that. But when God finishes with it, it will become no more than an idol to those who continue in it.

Council members: *Comments.*

Paul: The law has been a precious gift from God, a blessing, a guardian to prepare us for the coming of . . .

Eli: First, a warden, and now, a guardian, a hireling! What other vile title will you give to the holy law which Moses said is our life? No wonder you and Barnabas rely so little on the law to teach your doctrine; it is not your life; it is just your "guardian" – or used to be. You've outgrown it now, or so you think. But how can a man outgrow God? Look at the multitude of scriptures that testify against you! Do you and Barnabas think that you and your little group are the only ones right, and the whole Assembly of God is wrong?

Paul: We do not say that we are right. Nor do we say that you, or any man, is right. We say that God alone is right. And He has authority to forbid today what He commanded yesterday, to make wrong today what was right yesterday. My gospel justifies no one but God, and we glory in nothing but His work through His Son.

---

[256] In the books of Exodus, Leviticus, and Numbers.

[257] Ps. 115:8; 135:18.

Hushai: Why have you and Barnabas turned against your own nation?

Paul: My nation is the nation whom God has chosen and sanctified for Himself by His Spirit.

Maschil: But God chose *Israel* to be His nation! Have you forgotten what David said: "The LORD has chosen Jacob for Himself, and Israel as His peculiar treasure"?[258]

Paul: Not all who are in Israel are part of the Israel of God. God is creating for Himself a new Israel, a nation of people born of the Spirit, as David said, "They shall declare His righteousness to a people that shall be born."[259]

Hushai: You are clever, Paul. The Greeks would revel in this verbal sparring of yours, straining at gnats and swallowing camels, just as Jesus said about other blind guides.[260] As for me, I am growing weary of this foolishness. Our nation has suffered terrible judgments from God because of crafty men who persuaded our fathers to forsake His law. And now, you would bring upon us the same condemnation!

Paul: There can never be any condemnation to those who walk in the Spirit with Jesus.

Hushai: There will most certainly be condemnation on those who refuse the law! God said so! You know the scriptures! How many times does God have to say it before you will believe it?

Paul: I believe everything that God has ever said. I believe Moses, and I believe the prophets. And I believe Solomon, who said that there is a time for everything under the sun.[261] And I am telling you that the law's time will soon end.

The Need for Revelation

Micah: Then, you and Barnabas must have a revelation concerning when the law will be no more.

Barnabas: No, that is in God's hand. He has not shown us when, only that the time will come. It may or may not be in our lifetime. God makes His own plans.

Micah: And until that time comes, you say that we Jews must continue in temple worship?

Barnabas: Yes.

---

[258] Ps. 135:4.

[259] Ps. 22:31.

[260] Mt. 23:24.

[261] Eccl. 3:1.

Micah: But in some unknown time in the future, all who believe will worship God without the law of Moses, and nothing will remain but your new gospel.

Barnabas: Yes. And then there will be unity in faith and practice among all believers, provided that all walk in the Spirit. It is foretold in the prophets.

Micah: We understand that you think so.

Daniel: To understand the scriptures, Micah, requires the same anointing that it took to write them. We understand nothing without revelation. Every generation must have fresh revelation because every generation must learn God for itself; there is no other way to know Him but by experience. The greatest curse is silence from heaven, which brings upon men the greatest sickness: confusion of heart.

Micah: I need a revelation, then, brother Daniel, for what Barnabas is saying seems . . . But perhaps I should only repeat what Jesus said to some of our rulers one day in the temple when they questioned how he came to possess such knowledge of the scriptures without being trained. He told them that he received his doctrine from God, and then added, "He who speaks on his own is seeking his own glory."[262]

John: Yes, Micah, I noted that, too. It was during a Feast of Tabernacles. On the last day of the Feast, Jesus told his accusers that he was not seeking his own glory.[263]

Micah: Amen! Jesus certainly was not seeking his own glory, and I desire to be like him. I just want God to help me see who is seeking his own glory here, today, in this meeting. Somebody is.

Council members: *Comments.*

Hushai: How can there be any question as to who that is, Micah? Whose doctrine contradicts the law and the prophets? Whose doctrine has never been heard of? It is as plain as day to me who is speaking on his own today.

Council members: *Comments.*

The Nature of the Law

Hananiah: Brothers, this new doctrine, that we who are circumcised will be required to cease from God's holy law, is astonishing; it grieves my Spirit, and I believe God's as well. Let me try to reason with you who believe this thing, in the simplest terms I can muster.

---

[262] Jn. 7:18a.
[263] Jn. 8:50.

Moses' law is holy because the God who gave it is holy. Likewise, it is eternal, seeing that God is eternal. Solomon said that everything God does is eternal and that nothing can be added to or taken from it,[264] though many have tried to do so. They have all failed, thanks be to God, and this new doctrine will fail, too. Many times, God said through the prophets that His statutes were eternal. Think about the words of David: "God has sent a ransom for His people; He has commanded His covenant forever."[265] This, dear brothers, is what God has done! He has sent His Son to ransom us and to establish forever the covenant God gave to our fathers. God said it, and He did it. That is the sum of what we are saying, and it was all that we were telling the Gentiles in Antioch before Barnabas and Paul stopped us.

Benjamin: And what about our history, brother Paul? Every time Israel has ceased keeping the law, God cursed the nation.

Paul: That was because the Son had not yet fulfilled the law, Benjamin. It was not time for Israel to cease from keeping it, and until God finishes with it, it will remain that way, and it will remain sinful for us *not* to keep it.

Benjamin: But why would Solomon declare that whatever God does is eternal if He has done something that is not eternal, as you teach? Men construct houses that collapse; men make laws that are overridden; men build kingdoms that are overthrown, but not God.

Lamech: That's good, Benjamin. God is eternal, and all His works are eternal. Keep your eyes on the scriptures, son. They are the bedrock of genuine faith. Jesus is showing you that, too. I can see it.

Benjamin: Oh no, sir; I'll never forget the scriptures. At the same time, what about the way I am feeling? My heart is telling me there is something good and right in what Paul and Barnabas and the others are saying. I just can't make out the whole picture.

Lamech: Perhaps I can clear things up for you. Consider the act of prophecy itself. The prophets prophesied of Messiah's coming, and yet, we still prophesy, do we not?

Benjamin: Yes.

Lamech: Then, if we still prophesy *after* Messiah has come, Messiah's coming did not do away with prophecy, did it?

Benjamin: It obviously did not.

Lamech: But the law also prophesied of Messiah, Benjamin. The difference between the two is that the law prophesied with its rites while

---

[264] Eccl. 3:14.
[265] Ps. 111:9.

the prophets prophesied with their words. And yet, these men teach that Messiah is doing away with the law.

Benjamin: [*slowly*] That is true.

Paul: But there is a difference, Lamech. For there are prophecies yet to be fulfilled and events still to be prophesied about, and the LORD would still have us to know what lies ahead. But there will never again be a handwritten law of rites and rules for God's people. There is a difference.

Hillel: There is also a difference, Paul, between clever manipulation of the scriptures and revelation of their true meaning. One glorifies God, and the other glorifies the cunning of men. Did God not reveal the law to Moses? Or did He not reveal His word to the prophets? Of course He did! Therefore, to live by the law and the prophets is to live by the revelation of God.

God's statutes and judgments were revealed in order to prepare us for the coming of the Son of God, who has now engraved those same statutes and judgments on our hearts. Jesus implied that everyone who trusted Moses was righteous in God's sight, for he said that whoever believed in Moses would also believe in him, for Moses wrote of him.[266]   That is Jesus' gospel, and it is ours! Every man in this room obtained grace to partake of this new covenant because we believed in Moses first and partook of that covenant!

Council members: *Comments.*

Benjamin: What? I don't . . .

Barnabas: But which covenant is eternal, Hillel?

Hillel: They are parts of the same work of God, Barnabas; they go together. The prophets said so!

Micah: If the law is not eternal, Barnabas, why did David say to God, "I will keep your law always, for ever and ever!"[267] And why did God say to Moses, "Oh, that they had such a heart in them, to fear me always and to keep all my commandments!"[268] Of the Passover, God said, "*You* shall keep it as a feast to the LORD throughout *your* generations."[269] And of the Sabbath, God said, "It is a sign between me and the children of Israel forever."[270] And He whose breath made the heavens declared Aaron's priesthood to be an everlasting priesthood,[271] saying to Moses, "You shall gird

---

266 Jn. 5:46.

267 Ps. 119:44.

268 Dt. 5:29a.

269 Ex. 12:14b.

270 Ex. 31:17a.

271 Ex. 40:15.

Aaron and his sons, and the priesthood shall be theirs by statute forever."[272]   And when Solomon lifted up his voice at the dedication of God's temple, and declared before God, "I have built you a majestic house, an established place for you to dwell in forever and ever,"[273] what was God's response?   "I have heard your prayer and your supplication which you have made before me, and I have sanctified this house that you built, to put my name there forever, and my eyes and my heart will always be there."[274]

Barnabas: But "forever" can mean for an appointed length of time, Micah.

Nadab: You have no authority to re-define "forever", just so you can justify your doctrine.

Jared: No, Nadab; Barnabas is correct.   In the law, "forever" can mean for a long time[275] or for just a lifetime.[276]   What Barnabas is saying is that since Jesus is our heavenly high priest, Aaron's earthly priesthood must end.

Council members: *Comments.*

Paul: If a change is made in the priesthood, brother Jared, there must be a change made in the law.

Hushai: There has been no change made in God's *earthly* priesthood, Paul.   Jesus is a high priest *in heaven*.   That is a lie!

Hananiah: Hushai, no.   Please, brother.

Hushai: Do you hear this man, Hananiah?   It is outrageous!

Hananiah: I know.   I know.   But please, brother, let me respond.

Paul, there may be some truth in what you say, but truth carried beyond the boundaries set by God becomes something other than truth, and can be poisonous.   We all know that Jesus is our heavenly high priest, but Jesus never presumed to act as a priest while he was here on earth.   He acknowledged God's Levitical priesthood and became a priest himself only after he ascended into heaven, as the prophet said, "On his throne, he shall be a priest."[277]

Barnabas: And that being done, what need have we for an earthly priesthood, Hananiah? God had a purpose for Aaron's priesthood, but Jesus fulfilled that purpose.

---

[272] Ex. 29:9a.

[273] 1Kgs. 8:13.

[274] 1Kgs. 9:3.

[275] E.g., Ps. 143:3.

[276] E.g., Ex. 21:6.

[277] Zech. 6:13b.

Hananiah: With God, all things are eternal,[278] Barnabas, even His purposes, and if everything God does is eternal, then all we need to find out is what He has done, and then walk in it.

Hushai: That's right, Hananiah.

Circumcision and Baptism

Hananiah: One of the things God has done is to command father Abraham, "Every male among *you* shall be circumcised throughout *your* generations. And an uncircumcised male shall be cut off from his people, for he has broken my covenant."[279]

Barnabas: But God counted Abraham righteous before he was circumcised.[280]

Hillel: . . . as well as *after* he was circumcised. What you are saying is *our* point, Barnabas, not yours, and it is what we were teaching the Gentiles in Antioch when you and Paul stopped us. We were telling them to follow Abraham's example and receive circumcision as a sign of their righteousness. Would to God that Cornelius had been told to follow that example!

Barnabas: But the point, Hillel, is that God gave circumcision to Abraham *because* he was a righteous man, not in order to make him one.

Lamech: Of course, Barnabas! But did Abraham become *unrighteous* by receiving circumcision? The truth we were teaching the Gentiles in Antioch aligns perfectly with Abraham's experience. They were doing righteousness before we arrived, and they needed circumcision to *continue in righteousness*, just as Abraham needed it.

Paul: But ask yourself, what did Abraham need circumcision for if he was already righteous?

Lamech: I just told you! He needed circumcision in order to *continue* in the will of God. He had obeyed God before then; why should he have stopped obeying God? You would make the Gentiles stop obeying God as soon as He gives them the Spirit as witness that they *have* obeyed Him. Do you not remember what the Lord said, "He who endures to the end shall be saved"?[281]

Paul: Of course I remember. But can you tell me *God's* purpose for commanding righteous Abraham to be circumcised?

---

[278] Eccl. 3:14.

[279] Gen. 17:10, 14.

[280] God judged Abraham to be righteous in Genesis 15:6, but did not make the covenant of circumcision with him until Genesis 17:10.

[281] Mt. 24:13; Mk. 13:13.

Simeon: I can. God gave Abraham circumcision as an outward expression of an inward experience.

Bartholomew: Where in the world did you get such a doctrine, Simeon?

Simeon: It just came to me.

Eli: Maybe it's another new revelation, Bartholomew. Or do you not believe in that?

Micah: Brothers, I think there is truth in what Simeon said. After all, isn't it the same with the law? And even John's baptism? God sent John to baptize people as confirmation of the righteousness of those people *before* he baptized them; it was a holy sign to all that they had truly repented.

Lamech: That's why John refused baptism to the unrighteous when they came to him.[282] They were unworthy of it.

Hillel, Eli, Hilkiah, Nadab, Hushai, Hananiah, Benjamin, Maschil: *Amen. That is right. Etc.*

Simeon: I mean, if you think about it, what good is an inward experience without an outward expression of it?

Paul: It is no good at all without *any* outward expression, Simeon. But the outward expression of our inward experience in this covenant is holy living, not carrying out another dead ceremony.

Jacobus: Amen, Paul. Good works are the evidence of genuine faith, and faith without those works is dead.

Paul: Besides, you men are mistaken about circumcision and baptism being outward expressions of an inward experience.

Micah: How can that be so, Paul?

Paul: God gave circumcision as an outward expression of father Abraham's *lack* of an inward experience. That circumcision of the flesh was a testimony that Messiah had not yet brought in his circumcision of the heart. And for us to continue in that dead work after Messiah has come and fulfilled it is to deny him, for the Spirit alone bears witness that he came and that it was Jesus.

Council members: *Comments.*

Barnabas: Amen, Paul. God likewise sent John with his outward baptism of the flesh because Messiah had not yet given his inward baptism of the Spirit. But when Jesus began baptizing with the Spirit, God's purpose for John's baptism was fulfilled, making it unnecessary.

Hushai: But your conclusion is unjustified, Barnabas. Nothing that you or Paul has said forces the conclusion that Jesus' circumcision makes

---

[282] Mt. 3:7.

Abraham's circumcision null and void, or that Jesus' baptism makes John's baptism null and void.   John's baptism was a prophetic symbol, yes, but God still commands it of everyone who believes, and every man in this room has received it.

Council members: *Comments.*

Hushai: Peter preached the true gospel the day the Spirit first came, and it is still the true gospel. The word of the Lord that day and forever is this: "Repent and be baptized, every one of *you*, in the name of Messiah Jesus for the forgiveness of your sins, and *you* will receive the gift of the holy Spirit!"[283]

What Carnal Means

Paul: We have told you, Hushai, that, the law's works are not eternal, for they employ carnal things, and as sons of the living God, we are no more subject to carnal rites and rules than Jesus is now, in heaven.

Benjamin: Forgive me, Paul, for interrupting, but what exactly do you mean by "carnal rites and rules"?

Paul: I mean anything that is of this world.

Benjamin: Anything natural?

Paul: Yes; natural, earthly, fleshly – anything not of the Spirit.

Benjamin: And John's baptism, because it uses a carnal substance, water?

Paul: Yes.

Benjamin: What about the temple, and the sacrifices God gave us in the law?

Paul: It is the same. Messiah has been sacrificed for us.

Benjamin: And the Passover feast?

Paul: Jesus is our Passover Lamb, and we live by eating of him and drinking of the Spirit.

John: This is what Jesus meant, Benjamin, when he said that we must eat his flesh and drink his blood if we would have eternal life, just as he ate of the Father and lived by Him.[284]

Micah: We can agree with all that, John. Our unanswered question is, why not do both? Jesus did. Did you and I not eat with Jesus at the feasts and make our offerings at the temple that the law requires? John baptized you and me with water, and Jesus baptized us both with the Spirit. So, why should we think that the coming of the spiritual does away with the

---

[283] Acts 2:38.
[284] Jn. 6:53–57.

carnal? It seems to me that the natural and the spiritual should dwell together in peace. That is how Jesus lived, under the law and in the Spirit, and that is how we have been living these past decades, in peace with one another.

Council members: *Comments.*

Micah: I do not doubt our brothers' testimony of being sent to the heathen. Indeed, I am glad for it. But it seems to me that they have carried whatever it was that Jesus showed them too far. We can do that sometimes, in an excess of exuberance.

In Jesus' Name

Paul: We have not gone too far, Micah. Everything that God ever used as a light for men was a harbinger of the light of His Son.

Maschil: That is another example of you stretching truth beyond its intended purpose. We all know that Moses and the prophets spoke of Messiah Jesus, but you say that everything God ever did through His servants spoke of him. How can that be true?

Paul: I will explain, Maschil. I have a question for those of you here who were baptized by John before Jesus came to John from Galilee to be baptized. When John baptized you, in whose name did he baptize you?

Joseph: Why, in Jesus' name, just as we do now.

Paul: I mean before John ever saw Jesus. In whose name did he say he was baptizing then? You were baptized by John during those days. What did he say to you, Joseph?

Joseph: Oh, I see. Well, he didn't use Jesus' name, of course, since he didn't yet know who Messiah would be. So, he said things like, "I baptize you with water, but a man is coming after me who is greater than I am. He will baptize you with the holy Ghost and fire."[285]

John: John told us all plainly that he did not know who it was that was coming after him, that is, until he saw a heavenly dove descend and light upon Jesus.[286] After that, he started baptizing in Jesus' name, but before that, he never did.

Paul: Andrew and Simon, you were baptized before Jesus came to John, were you not?

Andrew: Yes.

Simon Peter: Not long before, yes.

---

[285] Cf. Mt. 3:11; Mk. 1:7–8; Lk. 3:16; Jn. 1:15, 26–27.
[286] Jn. 1:32–33.

Paul: And did John baptize you the way he baptized brother Joseph, not using a specific name? Is that how he baptized you?

Andrew and Simon Peter: Yes.

Paul: But after Jesus came and was baptized by John, and John saw the dove and knew Jesus was Messiah, how did his baptism change?

Joseph: His baptism remained the same; only the words changed. After he knew who Messiah was, he told the people, "I baptize you in the name of Jesus of Nazareth."

Paul: And is that how John baptized you, Hananiah? You were baptized after Jesus was, if I heard right.

Hananiah: That's right.

Paul: Did John say, when he baptized you, "I baptize you in Jesus' name," or did he continue to say, "I baptize you in the name of the one who is coming after me?"

Hananiah: He said, "In Jesus' name," of course. And that is how John's baptism was administered from the day he met Jesus until now.

Council members: *Amen. That's true. Etc.*

Paul: Yes, that is how Ananias baptized me, too, in Damascus. For we all knew by then who Messiah is.

Council members: *Amen. That's true. Etc.*

Paul: So now, I have a question for those of you who were baptized by John before he met Jesus and found out he was our Messiah. After John met Jesus and began baptizing in Jesus' name, did you feel that your baptism was not good enough? Did you go back to the Jordan to ask John to re-baptize you – this time in Jesus' name – or did you feel satisfied that God's will had been fully done?

Joseph: I would have felt ashamed to ask him to re-baptize me. I knew it had been accepted in God's sight, and I am certain John would not have re-baptized us even if we had asked him. John baptized only as he was directed by the Spirit; he never baptized the wrong person. If the Spirit did not approve of a person, John sent them away; he always discerned who had truly repented. What John did was irreversible, as was Isaac's blessing on Jacob. The Spirit moved Isaac to bless him, and Isaac could not take it back after he learned he had blessed Jacob instead of Esau, as he had intended.[287] So it was with John's baptism; once the Spirit moved him to baptize someone, it was sealed in heaven.

Paul: And I ask you, in whose name was it sealed in heaven?

Joseph: Why, I suppose in the name of Jesus, even if John did not say it.

---

[287] Gen. 27:30–37.

Paul: I agree. John's baptism was done in Jesus' name because God knew His Son's name even if John did not.

Council members: *Comments.*

Paul: But that is just one example of the truth I am trying to get across. Every blessing that God has given to man since the foundation of the world, every prophecy, every wise saying, every miracle has been given in the name of Jesus. God never mentioned the name of His Son because He was keeping him hidden until our time, but God knew him, and God was the One doing the work. Just as every man John ever baptized was, in truth, baptized in the name of Jesus, so every man who ever followed the law was following the law in Jesus' name. The fact that those who kept the law did not know the name of Jesus made no difference, for the God who gave the law knew. Moses did not know the name of Jesus, but he, like John at the beginning of his work, told Israel he was preparing them for another who was coming after him. He said, "A prophet like me shall the LORD your God raise up for you, from among your kinsmen; to him, you must listen!"[288] Moses said that in Jesus's name.

Paul: At the foundation of the world, when the Spirit of God moved over the face of the deep, it moved in the name of Jesus. At God's command, Joshua conquered this land in the name of Jesus! What difference did it make what Joshua knew? God knew His Son was coming to live in it! The Spirit of God came upon Elijah to judge the prophets of Baal, and he slaughtered four hundred of them in the name of Jesus.[289] The Spirit anointed David to sing in Jesus' name, and David sang, "My God, my God! They pierced my hands and my feet!"[290] The Spirit moved Isaiah to prophesy that a virgin would bear a son;[291] was that not done in Jesus' name? And Isaiah, again in Jesus' name, cried out, "We all, like sheep, have gone astray, and the LORD has laid upon him the iniquity of us all."[292] Was Isaiah prophesying in his own name? No, brothers, no more than John was baptizing in his own name before he met Jesus.

In truth, brothers, mine is no new gospel. It is the first, and the only gospel of God. Noah preached it to the world when he built his ark; Samuel preached it to Agag when he hacked that wicked king to pieces.[293] Elisha's dead bones preached it to the dead man whose corpse was thrown

---

[288] Dt. 18:15.

[289] 1Kgs. 18:22, 40.

[290] Ps. 22:1a, 16b.

[291] Isa. 7:14.

[292] Isa. 53:6.

[293] 1Sam. 15:32–33.

on them, and the dead man awoke from the dead in Jesus' name and stood on his feet.[294]   Daniel preached my gospel to the lions, and it shut their mouths so that they could not harm him.   All those things were done in Jesus' name by the God who knew his name.

Now, Noah did not have the Spirit within him, brothers; it only came upon him and gave him wisdom and power to accomplish his mission from God.   And Samuel and the prophets did not have it; they were only moved by the Spirit to say and do the things God appointed to them.   Neither did Moses have the Spirit, but it was upon him, for God said to him in the wilderness, "I will take some of the Spirit that is on you and put it on them."[295]   But the night before Jesus suffered, he told you disciples that the Father would send the Spirit in his name to dwell *within* you – and now, the same Spirit that moved over the waters in Jesus' name has filled us with the righteousness and peace and joy of God in Jesus' name!

Why do some of you now, born of the Spirit of the living God, want to continue forever to act as if you do not have the Spirit, performing dead rites, like men playing with children's toys?   Grow up!   Why do you want to act like Moses, who did not even know the name of Jesus, or like Abraham, bound in his ignorance, longing for the day Messiah would come?[296]   What is so great about their ignorance that you are not satisfied with the knowledge of the Son of God?   Jesus said that to know the Father and the Son is eternal life.[297]   What does this holy life lack, that you cling so tightly to dead works?

In great mercy, God is tolerating for a little while the Jews' superstitious fear by allowing Israel to continue in the ways of our fathers who did not know His Son.   But He will not allow Moses and the prophets to share in His Son's glory forever, and if God ever opens your eyes to see His Son's majesty, you will marvel that He has even allowed us this much time to continue in the dead works of Moses' law.

Hillel Condemns Paul's Doctrine as Heathen Philosophy

Lamech: It is not superstitious fear that motivates me to keep the law, Paul, nor it is anyone's motivation who loves God.

Council members: *Comments.*

---

[294] 2Kgs. 13:20–21.

[295] Num. 11:17.

[296] Jn. 8:56.

[297] Jn. 17:3.

Paul: I understand how you men are looking at this. What you are thinking is what I once thought. But Jesus taught me truth that I did not expect, and wasn't even asking for!

Hillel: He may have, Paul, but truth can be put to a wrong purpose. I mean no comparison with you personally, but you know that Satan used truth during the Temptation of Jesus.

Council members: *Comments*.

Paul: No offense taken, Hillel. But I would say that Satan *abused* truth during the Temptation, rather than used it.

Hillel: I agree, but my point is that to simply proclaim this or that to be true, the way Gentile philosophers do, or to craftily pick out a few scriptures, as Satan did in the wilderness, instead of relying upon the whole counsel of God is not the way of God. It is the way of those who do not love Him and His law. Some of your reasonings are appealing, but then I have to ask myself, what false teacher ever gained a following without appealing words?

Hushai: Yes, no matter how appealing your doctrine sounds, Paul, unless it is a reflection of the law and the prophets, how can we think anything but that you have been influenced by the Gentiles to devise a new philosophy, or as Hillel suggested, inspired by Satan to teach a doctrine of demons? The law and the prophets testified of Messiah Jesus, and we can see him clearly in them. But where are you and Barnabas in the law? Where are you and Barnabas in Isaiah, or Jeremiah, or the other prophets?

David was not speaking of a heavenly temple when he said, "O LORD, I love the site of your house, even the place of the tabernacle of your glory!"[298] And what city but this one could David have been speaking about when he said to God, "Your servants take pleasure in her stones and favor her dust"?[299] Heaven has no dust, Paul.

I hear the good things you say about Messiah Jesus; I see your passion for serving God. But you have taken things beyond the bounds of all reason. You spiritualize things that God never meant to be spiritualized. And you have yet to explain to us why Messiah would bring about the end of the law – and now, not only for the Gentiles, but for us Jews as well!

Paul: My gospel is no philosophy, Hushai. And Satan has no part in it. If my gospel seems to be against reason, it is only because you are trying to understand the things of God with a carnal mind, which cannot fathom the things of God. My gospel came by revelation, and I see it in the law and in all the prophets. But even if I did not see it there, I would

---

[298] Ps. 26:8.
[299] Ps. 102:14.

still know it is true because I see my gospel in *Jesus!* Jesus ministers salvation with heavenly, not earthly things, and the glory God has given His Son makes all earthly things worthless for salvation. When we were re-created as God's sons, we were freed from reliance upon fleshly things, liberated to serve God in spirit, as Jesus serves Him now.

Lamech: How far should we take this notion of yours, Paul? If we are to be as Jesus is now, we should stop eating and drinking, since Jesus no longer consumes carnal food and drink.

Paul: The kingdom of God is not in food and drink, Lamech, but in righteousness, and peace, and joy in God's holy Spirit, and whoever serves Messiah Jesus in those things is acceptable to God, whether circumcised or not.

Micah: If we love God and do what His law teaches, we *must* be living the way God desires for us to live. He asks nothing more, for the prophet said, "What does the LORD require of you, but to do justice, and to love mercy, and to walk humbly with your God?"[300] That was not the prophet's idea; it was the revelation of God to him. It was the way he himself lived his life. Do you think the prophets lived contrary to the way Moses commanded?

Paul: They loved the law and obeyed it, but they were not transformed by it. They were never born of God, as Jesus said men must be. But the Spirit has come now, and it has made us new creatures that can sense God's will without handwritten rules telling us what it is. And if that is done, what need is there for handwritten rules?

The Limitation of a Handwritten Law

Maschil: But if the Spirit has made us able to fully comprehend and to do God's will, then why stop keeping the law that tells us to do it?

Paul: Because we do not need a handwritten law to tell us what the Spirit is already saying in our hearts. God's children do not need a handwritten list of rules if they are walking by the law of the Spirit.

Lamech: What is this "law of the Spirit" that you keep talking about? Which prophet ever declared the Spirit would bring a different law with it when it came?

Paul: Not a different law; the same law in a different way.

Eli: What prophet ever promised that?

Paul: All of them did, if you have eyes to see!

Eli: I see Jesus in the prophets; I do not see your doctrine!

---

[300] Mic. 6:8.

Nathan: You can rest assured, Barnabas and Paul, that we honor your zeal and your great efforts to spread the good news of Messiah Jesus. Don't we, brothers?

Council members: *Comments.*

Paul: I am not here to receive honor. I am here to give honor to the Son of God.

Hananiah: We have agreed with you, Paul, that when we receive the Spirit, God writes His law in our hearts. But by writing His law in our hearts, isn't God confirming the law for us and making us doubly bound to keep it? Why would God write a law in our hearts that He does not want us to keep? But you are teaching men who receive the Spirit to forsake the very law that God writes in their heart!

John: How can we ever forsake it, Hananiah, if God has written it on our hearts?

Hilkiah: But that is *our* point, John. How can we forsake something that God has written on our hearts? It would be unnatural to live contrary to our nature.

Council members: *Comments.*

Andrew: You are looking at it the wrong way, Hilkiah.

Jared: It makes perfect sense to me.

Hushai: It makes perfect sense to every wise soul. What Paul and Barnabas teach contradicts the scriptures! And so far, their chief response to the law and the prophets has been a philosophical exposition based upon their claim of a new revelation. And they still have not explained why the coming of Messiah, however great God has made him, means that the law and the prophets who foretold his coming must now be cast aside.

Barnabas: Brothers, please. Paul and I are only testifying to what we have heard from the Lord.

Nadab: That will be for this council to decide!

Paul: I did not come here for this Council to decide if my gospel was of God. I came to hear them tell you that it is. My gospel is not just a debatable possibility. If an angel were to come out of heaven with a gospel contrary to my gospel, I would consider him accursed!

Council members: *Loud comments.*

Barnabas: Brothers! Brothers! Paul is only saying what must be said! We mean no disrespect to anyone, but the gospel Jesus gave us is not of ourselves. It came from heaven!

Hananiah: But Barnabas, your message is contrary to the law and the prophets.

Barnabas: It is not contrary to them at all in our eyes.

Apostles: *Nor to ours. Amen! That's right. Etc.*

Jesus' Example of Keeping the Law

Hushai: If Jesus was the prophet of whom Moses spoke when he said, "A prophet like me will the LORD your God raise up,"[301] then, can anyone tell me how is Jesus like Moses if he is *not* like him? Moses commanded men to keep the law forever, but the Jesus that Barnabas and Paul preach commands men not to keep it!

Lamech: That is not the Jesus that any of us knew and followed.

Hillel: Amen! I followed the Jesus who knew and kept the law, and I still follow him!

Benjamin: How can I justify abandoning the law, brother Barnabas, if God sent His Son to be a Jew like us?

Barnabas: I understand, Benjamin. But tell me, my friend, what makes a man a Jew?

Benjamin: Circumcision, of course.

Barnabas: Then, if as Jesus said, children of the resurrection do not marry,[302] do you think that a glorified body has a member that *can* be circumcised? Or is such a glorified body neither male nor female, like God?

Benjamin: I would think it is like God.

Barnabas: Then, if circumcision makes a man a Jew, how is Jesus still a Jew if he has a glorified body like his Father instead of a circumcised one like us?

Benjamin: I see what you are saying, I think.

Barnabas: That is why we teach that the Israel of God are they who walk in the Spirit, whether their earthly bodies be circumcised or not. No earthly condition defines the children of God in this covenant; the Spirit defines us when we receive it.

Paul: We are to follow Jesus as he is now, not as he used to be.

Maschil: What do you mean, Paul?

Paul: We have known Jesus as a man, subject to death and the elements of this world, but we will never know him that way again. He will never again subject himself to carnal things; he is the end of the law for us who believe.

Hilkiah: Paul, but it sounds as if you think that you and your Gentile disciples have gone deeper than Jesus.

---

[301] Dt. 18:15a.

[302] Lk. 20:34–36.

Council members: *Comments.*

Paul: We need only go as deep as Jesus is, Hilkiah, and then we will see the truth.

Maschil: But why would God have given us circumcision and the law to make us what His Son was not, and then send His Son down from heaven to make him what we are? If God would have us to follow in His Son's footsteps, what does it mean that God made His Son a Jew?

Paul: God gave us the law that spoke of His Son to prepare us for His Son; then, He sent His Son here to be like us so that through him, we might become sons of God, as he is. God's purpose was not to make His Son forever like us, but to make us forever like His Son.

Maschil: I am sorry, but your answers confuse me.

Hillel: Confused men give confusing answers, Maschil, and the most confused men give the most confusing answers.

Hushai: Your question was a good one, Maschil, for it penetrates the haze of this philosophical wrangling. Where are the scriptures for that answer?

Lamech: We are asked to believe things that no man of God has ever said, even Jesus himself.

Barnabas: If Jesus opens your eyes, as he did mine, you will see what we teach in the scriptures.

John: Lamech, after Messiah's last meal, he prayed earnestly that the Father would restore him to the glory he had with Him from the foundation of the world.[303] What does that mean, except that he wanted to return to his former state when he was not circumcised nor subject to the law and the sufferings of this life?

Paul: And when the Father welcomed him home and glorified him again, Messiah found himself again in the form of God, as he had been since before the world began, neither Jew nor Gentile. The only difference now is that he has tasted of our kind of life, and he did that only so that he could die and become a sacrifice for our sins. And from the day Jesus made his sacrifice in heaven, sacrifices of earthly animals became useless for salvation. How can an ox compare with the sacrifice of God's Son? That is truth that Jesus revealed to me.

Hananiah: It may be that in his glorified form, Messiah is not observing the forms of the law, for earthly elements are not in heaven. But Messiah was neither Jew nor Gentile when God commanded Abraham to be circumcised. And he was neither Jew nor Gentile when God commanded Israel to observe the law. So, what does Messiah's being

---

[303] Jn. 17:5.

neither Jew nor Gentile *in heaven* have to do with us who are here on earth? God commands men *on earth* to be circumcised and to keep the law because that is what men on earth need. What God demands now of Jesus in heaven says nothing about what we who are still on earth must do.

Regardless of Messiah's present or past state in heaven, no one can deny that God's commandments applied to him while he was on earth like us. The issue is not whether or not Jesus is keeping the law now, in heaven. The issue is, what did God require of Jesus while he was here on earth, so that he might attain to the blessed state he is in now, in the presence of God? And the answer is clear; he attained to his great glory by obeying God's law. And that is what God requires of all men!

Benjamin: That is what I was trying to say. We are not heavenly beings, Paul; we are men.

Barnabas: Messiah observed the law because God sent him to Israel, where the law was. If God had sent him to Egypt, He would not have commanded him to do that.

Hananiah: But God did not send him to Egypt because there was no light of God there. Instead, He sent him to Israel, to His law, that His Son might be an example to the heathen, as the prophets said, "I will give you for a covenant for the people and for a light of the nations."[304] And if Messiah kept the law as a light to the heathen, who will be their light now if none of us keep it?

Paul: Whoever walks in the Spirit is a light for all men, Hananiah.

John: Jesus was the light of the world because the life of God was in him.[305] His flesh was not the light of the world. That is why nobody knew who he was; men only saw the flesh that the Son of God had taken upon himself.

Micah: But, John, Jesus told us at the start that *we* were the light of the world,[306] and that was years before we received the Spirit.

John: But before the Spirit was given, walking by the law is what made us lights. Besides, we must judge all things by the perfect light which Messiah has now brought into this world. He is the light of God, and compared to his glory, all things that came before and spoke of him are nothing but darkness.

Council members: *Comments.*

----

[304] Isa. 42:6.

[305] Jn. 1:4.

[306] Mt. 5:14.

Hillel: All of this is wrong-headed, brothers. I am warning you! God is trying our hearts with all this, to see who will be faithful to Him and who will be drawn away! In spite of right-sounding things that have been said, there is poison in the pot! David prayed, "Give me understanding, that I might keep your law;"[307] then, a lack of understanding must lead men not to keep it. I do not mean to sound harsh, but by all that is holy, brothers! If "the law is truth," then how can a man who turns men from it be telling the truth? And "if the foundations be destroyed, what can the righteous do?"[308] How can anyone who loves God not cry out against this doctrine? Should not the righteous feel as righteous King David felt when he saw God's law being forsaken and cried out, "Hot indignation took hold of me!"[309]

Say what you will, I will not be persuaded. I love God's law and find peace in it. Hear me, brothers! God tested Jesus' heart in the wilderness by sending Satan to him, armed with scripture. And this new doctrine is a test of our hearts that God has sent to prove us! Pass the test! The foundation of our lives is the law and the prophets; without them, we are not ourselves; we are not God's chosen people. I am beginning to despair. Don't let these men do this to us!

Lamech, Eli, Hilkiah, Nadab, Hushai, Maschil: *Comments.*

Hillel: It is not at all that we oppose God's calling of the Gentiles, and we are pleased for Paul and Barnabas to go to them if that is their calling. But nothing that Paul and Barnabas have said, or what you have said, John, proves that God's calling of the Gentiles releases them from the duty of keeping His law. There was no exclusion made for Gentiles when Isaiah said the gospel would summon men to both the law and the Spirit.

Council members: *Comments.*

John: Barnabas and Paul are saying no more than what the Lord once told a Samaritan woman. Jesus told her that the time was at hand when true worshippers would worship the Father neither in Samaria nor in Jerusalem, but in spirit and in truth.[310] God was never worshipped that way by our fathers, for the Spirit had not come to make it possible, but now, God demands it.

Micah: We know that God demands that, John. Since the day you told me Jesus said that, I have never questioned it. But we *are* worshipping spiritually and truly now, John, when we worship according to the

---

[307] Ps. 119:34.

[308] Ps. 11:3.

[309] Ps. 119:53.

[310] Jn. 4:23–24.

law. Wasn't Jesus worshipping God spiritually and truly when he observed the law?

Paul: Yes, and his worship was acceptable, as yours is now, because it was God's will for him to keep the law, as it is also His will for you and me to keep it.

Maschil: But that does not explain why you say that God will bring an end to the law.

Micah: We see that Jesus has brought about the day of which he spoke to that woman, John, but worshipping God spiritually and truly is what Jesus always did, and it is what we are doing when we do as he did.

Paul: We agree with that, Micah. Nothing we teach contradicts what you just said.

Micah: But it does! For you say it will soon be wrong for Jews to live the way Jesus lived. How can it ever be evil to do *anything* the way Messiah did, whether it be to heal the sick, honor the Sabbath, or be circumcised? Messiah was sinless! How can we be wrong to follow his sinless example?

Council members: *Comments.*

Paul: Jesus' example was only to do the will of God, Micah, whatever that was, for when he left the Father to come into the world, he said, "I go to do your will, O God!"[311] And we follow his example by doing the will of God for us, in our time, whatever His will for us may be. Barnabas and I still look to Messiah as our example, and we are following His example when we follow the Spirit – and *only* then.

Maschil: Why, then, did Jesus even bother with keeping the law and bringing all this confusion into the world? I know I sound frustrated, but what you are saying sounds so complicated.

John: Maschil, if Messiah had lived on earth without the law, the way he had lived with the Father in heaven since the foundation of the world, even we who were his closest disciples would have rejected him.

Hillel: And rightly so. Why would you follow a man who did not obey the commandments of God?

Maschil: Are you saying, John, that Jesus kept the law just to keep Israel from rejecting him?

John: What better reason could there be than to shelter God's people from what would be too much for them?

Maschil: I am dumbfounded. Did Jesus ever talk like this with you disciples while he was here?

---

[311] Ps. 40:7.

Matthew: Other than in parables, no. If he had spoken then as plainly as we do now, we would have misjudged him and gone away.

Bartholomew: We would have thought he didn't love the law.

Philip: But he certainly did love it.

Matthew: Yes, he did.

Paul: And it is good and right for us to continue in the law for the time being, for if *we* cease from the law before God's time, what hope will our fellow Jews have of believing in Jesus? We would be stumbling blocks to them, instruments of their destruction, not salvation.

Barnabas: The gospel that Jesus preached, and which we all still preach to the Jews, is holy and good, but it will be of no more use when God finds no more people in Israel who will hear it, for that gospel will never be for the Gentiles.

Maschil: If this is the truth, I cannot see it.

Eli: You can't see it because it is not the truth, Maschil. You should be thankful that you don't see it.

God's Purpose for His Son Keeping the Law

Barnabas: Let me ask you men this. Could the Son of God, who was with God, rejoicing with Him before the world began, daily His delight,[312] have delighted the Father or been able to rejoice with Him if he had not been righteous?

Hillel: Of course not.

Barnabas: Well, where was Moses' law at that time?

Hillel: The law was within him! For he said through the prophet, "I delight to do your will, O my God, for your law is in my heart."[313]

Barnabas: And that is my point, Hillel. Because the Father's law of the Spirit was in him, it was the Son's *nature* to do the will of God. He did not need to come down to earth and submit to Moses' law in order to become righteous. He came and obeyed the law so that we would no longer be bound to it, but have God's kind of life within us, as he did – and he did all that only because it was the Father's will that he do it for our sakes.

John: Jesus' food was to do the will of God; he lived on that bread.[314] He once said that to us, but at the time, none of us knew what he was talking about.[315]

---

[312] Prov. 8:30.

[313] Ps. 40:8.

[314] Jn. 4:34.

[315] Jn. 4:32.

Lamech: Men and brothers! Where are the prophets' voices in any of this? Jesus kept the law because he loved God and wanted to please *Him*, not us! He was not making a show of submission to Moses' law for our sakes. Every righteous man since the days of Moses has loved and kept the law.

Paul: And what made them righteous, Lamech, but doing the will of God? Barnabas and I have acknowledged that it pleased God for our fathers to keep the law.

Hananiah: But you say that it is *not* God's will for the Gentiles to keep it and that it will soon not be His will for us to keep it, either! Jesus said, "*This* gospel of the kingdom will be preached in all the earth for a witness to all nations."[316] He said nothing about a different gospel being preached to the nations. He said "this gospel", and that must be the gospel he was preaching.

Barnabas: Hananiah, my dear friend, the only real difference between our gospel for the Gentiles and yours for the Jews is that our gospel excludes the carnal elements of the law. Other than that, ours is the same gospel that Jesus preached.

Hillel: Is the gospel Jesus preached not perfect? Does it not still heal and save? The gospel of Jesus needs no adjusting to accommodate the heathen. Don't tinker with it, Barnabas!

Lamech, Eli, Hilkiah, Nadab, Hushai, Hananiah, Benjamin, Maschil: *Comments.*

Jesus and the Samaritan Woman

Paul: Let me try to explain it this way: Jesus did more than die for us; he also lived for us. He was circumcised the eighth day for us; he kept the feast days for us; he honored the Sabbath for us; and those who believe in him do not need to do those things any more than they need to die for their own sins. Whoever is baptized with the Spirit is baptized into him, and if we are in him who kept the law for us and died for us, then we, through him, have kept the law and died, in the sight of God.

Hushai: This is rank philosophy!

Hillel: Messiah demonstrated for us how to live! Only a heathen philosopher could find a way to teach that men should not keep the law *because* Messiah kept it. This is perverse!

Council members: *Comments.*

---

[316] Mt. 24:14.

Paul: In Jesus is everything! In him we are born in spirit, circumcised in spirit, baptized in spirit, and enjoy the true Sabbath in spirit! In him, we are crucified, we are dead, we are buried, and we are raised up to sit with him among heavenly beings! We who are in Messiah Jesus do not need to keep the law in the flesh any more than we need to be nailed on a cross; Jesus did all that for us! In him, we are complete; we need no handwritten law when we are led by the Spirit.

Hillel: I must have been dozing, Paul. What were the scriptures again for all of this you were saying?

Paul: You have something better than the scriptures; you have the life of God inside of you, bearing witness to you that I am speaking the truth.

Council members: *Comments.*

Hillel: The life of God is telling me that He never said such things to His prophets.

Paul: It wasn't time for Him to say such things to the prophets, but He is saying such things to you, and you would do well to listen. What is the Spirit saying to you, Benjamin?

Benjamin: This is all very difficult to take in. It seems to glorify Messiah Jesus, but does it really, if it is contrary to the law, and if the prophets say nothing of it?

Paul: It seems contrary only when your mind has not been fully purged from dead works to serve the living God.

Benjamin: But I have never wanted to be purged from the law. How could I ever want such a thing?

Paul: When you and I keep the law, Benjamin, we are following Jesus' footsteps. We, like him, are clean without it, by the Spirit, and we, like him, are keeping it for the sake of our fellow Jews. And so, even after God closes the door on the law – and He will do it – we will still be able to follow Jesus' example by doing the will of God, whatever it is at that time. All that Jesus was really doing while he was here was God's will; that is all he has ever done. What is carnal cannot last forever, Benjamin, but what is in the Spirit is eternal.

Benjamin: But the scriptures . . . I just don't know any more.

Matthew: Benjamin, do you remember the woman in Samaria that John mentioned earlier?

Benjamin: Yes.

Matthew: We had stopped to rest at a well near Sychar. Jesus was so weary that he stayed at the well while we went into the town to buy food, and that's when she came out to draw water. When she saw that Jesus was a Jew, she began arguing that Jerusalem was not the only acceptable place of worship because Abraham, Isaac, and Jacob worshipped in the high places, and God accepted them.

Benjamin: But the scriptures say . . .

Matthew: Wait, please. You and I know what the scriptures say, but this is what I want you to do. I want you to put yourself and that woman back in King David's time, if you will. Can you imagine that for just a moment?

Benjamin: I suppose so. Yes, I will.

Matthew: Now, let's say that you are David, and the Samaritan woman approached you, as she approached Jesus at the well, and she began arguing with you, saying that worship in the high places is still acceptable to God, as it was in Abraham's day, and that Jerusalem is not the chosen place to worship. What would you say to her? But remember, God *revealed* to David that He had chosen Jerusalem as the place for His worship; David did not read that anywhere.

Council members: *Comments.*

Matthew: The scriptures that you started to mention a moment ago, the ones that say God chose Jerusalem as the only acceptable place of worship, were *written* by David and the prophets who came after him. So, you cannot point this woman to any of those scriptures. How would you, then, as David, convince her that Jerusalem is the only acceptable place for worship? What would you say to her?

Benjamin: [*slowly*] I don't know.

Matthew: But think on it. For whatever you would say to her is what you need to hear from us, and we are trying every way we can to say it.

Benjamin: I see what you are saying. King David could only tell the woman that God had spoken to him. All he had was his experience, his testimony of hearing from God.

Matthew: That's right.

Andrew: And beyond that, Benjamin, in that conversation at the well, Jesus told the woman that the one acceptable place of worship in this new covenant would be the heart, for the Spirit would come and dwell in us, making us the temple of God. I know how that sounds to some, but do you remember how it sounded to the judges when Stephen reminded them of what God once said through Isaiah: "Heaven is my throne, and the earth, my footstool. Where is this house that *you* would build for me?"[317]

Benjamin: They flew into a rage.

Andrew: . . . because they preferred their temple made of stones to the honor of becoming living temples of God.

---

[317] Isa. 66:1.

Benjamin: I looked up to Stephen as one would an older brother.

Andrew: I know you did, and Stephen loved you. But he had caught a glimpse of Messiah's glory, and his testimony provoked those proud judges. Messiah's glory will always provoke the proud to envy because they sense they have no part in it. But we have been given a part, Benjamin! We have been given a part in the kingdom of God! The Spirit has come and made us temples of God! Think of it! How can we praise him enough for grace *to be* the temple of God instead of having *to go* to it! We can make acceptable sacrifices to God right here in this room!

Council members: *Amen! Thank God! Praise God! Etc.*

Benjamin: It is a wonderful thing, brother Andrew. That feels good and right.

Andrew: It seems that I can still hear that sound from heaven, rushing down upon us the day the Spirit came! When I think of it, I am overwhelmed!

Council members: *Amen! Thank God! Praise God! Etc.*

Lamech: [*calmly, letting the feelings subside*] We were there, too, Andrew, when that sound came from heaven. We saw, with you and the others, the tongues of fire, and all of us felt the glory together. How holy an event that was! I am still in awe of it, too, and I praise God with you all.

But did God intend for that wonderful experience to become the be-all and end-all of life? Is the Spirit of God only within the bodies of those who believe? Is it not also in the temple? And if it is not there, why do you men still go to the temple to pray? No, wait. Don't tell me. It is only to be good examples for our fellow Jews, lest we cause them to stumble.

Council members: *Comments.*

The Limitation of Jesus' Power

Lamech: This is preposterous. Where is the evil in acknowledging the *two* temples of God, our bodies and the temple? That is how it was before these days, and there was peace.

Paul: We can continue in peace, Lamech, if we acknowledge one another's calling. You had no authority from God or from this Assembly to come to Antioch and tamper with the souls that God had placed in our care. I know you thought you were doing God service, but you did not know what you were doing. That is why I stopped you. What you were doing contradicted the fundamental truth I pointed out to you in the beginning: the unique power of Jesus to save.

Hushai: We know that Messiah is great, Paul, but God is greater.[318] Jesus has no power to undo anything God has done. He did not undo God's curse on Adam's race. Men are still appointed to die, and after that, they must all still face the Judgment.

Council members: *Comments.*

Hushai: And Jesus is not so great that he undid the distinction that God Himself made between us and the Gentiles. In Egypt, when God determined to spare Israel from the plague, He told Moses, "Against none of the children of Israel shall a dog wag its tongue, so that you may know that *the LORD makes a difference* between Egypt and Israel."[319] But now, this Council seems to be asking us to believe that when Jesus ascended to heaven, he did away with the difference that God made between us and the Gentiles – people whom Jesus himself called dogs![320]

Paul: Some of what you say is true, Hushai. Jesus did not undo the curse of death on our flesh or the fleshly distinction which God made between us and the Gentiles. But that was not God's purpose for sending him. What God sent Jesus to do was to make of both Jew and Gentile one new nation, and in the Spirit, he has done it. He has done away with that unscalable wall which God erected between us. And in this new nation, this new Israel of God, nothing of the flesh accomplishes anything for the soul. Jesus alone is Savior, and he saves by the Spirit alone.

Council members: *Comments.*

How Will End-time Prophecies Be Fulfilled?

Micah: But if the law ends, Paul, the Gentiles can never come join us, as the prophets all say they will do. What would they join? Without the law, Israel will not be Israel, but will be like the Gentiles, and God has always forbidden that. Oil and water do not mix, Paul; neither do circumcision and uncircumcision.

Jared: That is true, Micah. God commanded Israel not even to wear a cloak made from two kinds of cloth,[321] lest the stronger cloth cause the weaker to give way, and our nakedness be exposed. And He commanded us not to yoke an ox and an ass together,[322] lest the stronger beast work the weaker one to death. How then do we dare be yoked to the heathen

---

[318] Jn. 14:28.

[319] Ex. 11:7.

[320] Mt. 15:22–26.

[321] Dt. 22:11.

[322] Dt. 22:10.

and their ways? Let them come to us and fulfill the scriptures, and enjoy with us the blessings of God instead of His curse.

Council members: *Comments*.

Maschil: Yes, brother Paul, will it please God for us to be like the Gentiles, when He has commanded us not to learn the way of the heathen, nor do as they do?[323] What you are saying frightens me. You and others here are pressuring us to do something God has expressly forbidden, something that will certainly bring His fierce wrath down upon us!

Paul: Our message is not that God will make us like the Gentiles, nor that He will make the Gentiles like us. It is that by the Spirit, God has re-created us all, Jew and Gentile alike, to be like His Son. Yes, Micah, oil and water do not mix, but what if Jesus changes them both into wine? What then? There is no "oil and water" in Messiah Jesus. We are all one. Should the oil refuse to mix because of what it used to be?

Council members: *Comments*.

Paul: Yes, it is true that God commanded Israel not to be joined to foreigners, but Gentiles who are born of the Spirit are *not* foreigners to us, nor are we any longer foreign to them; we are citizens together of the kingdom of God. Those who do *not* believe, whether Jew or Gentile, are the foreigners, for they have no part in God's new Israel. We all are one in him who died for us.

Council members: *Comments*.

John: Amen.

Philip: Well said, Paul.

Barnabas' Warning

Barnabas: And we do not teach that Israel should live according to the customs of the Gentiles but that men should live by the dictates of the Spirit. Brothers, Paul and I are testifying of the gospel Jesus revealed to us. If you refuse our testimony and continue in the law after God finishes with it, God will forsake you and leave you with nothing but your law.

Hillel: It is not our law, Barnabas! It is God's law.

Paul: It will be yours when God finishes with it. And He *will* finish with it and leave it to the rebellious, as He said, "I will leave. I will return to my place until they admit their guilt and seek my face."[324] And in that day, He said, those who refuse the truth "will call on me, but I will not

---

[323] Jer. 10:2a.

[324] Hos. 5:15.

answer. They will seek me early, but they will not find me, forasmuch as they hated knowledge and did not choose the fear of the LORD."[325]

Hillel: No, Paul. Those scriptures were not intended to be used the way you are using them. Maschil was right. You are trying to seduce us to do something God has strictly forbidden. And I think I am beginning to see now why Jesus said Jerusalem will be destroyed and the nation crushed. It will be because of you! God forsook His holy place at Shiloh and cursed it because this people refused to keep His law,[326] and you would have God do the same to our temple and this holy city, for He said, "If *you* do not live by my law, I will make this house like Shiloh, and I will make this city a curse."[327] Jesus foresaw the rise of your doctrine, Paul, and foresaw you winning over these apostles and elders with your smooth talk, who then may persuade God's saints to forsake the law and bring upon this nation the fearful wrath of God. Was that not what David saw in the Spirit when he said, "It is time for the LORD to work. They have made your law of no effect"?[328] I am trying to save our nation, brothers! Hear me!

Council members: *Comments.*

Hillel: Earlier, Barnabas made much of brother Peter's question, "Who was I that I could withstand God?" Now, let me make much of it, too. God said, "Give ear, O my people, to my law!"[329] And I say, "Who are we, that we should withstand God and cease to hear it?" God said, "Do not forget my law!"[330] And I say, "Who are we, that we should withstand God and forget it?" God said, "Do not forsake my law!"[331] He said, "Keep my commandments, and live!"[332] And I say, Who are we, that we should withstand God, forsake His law, refuse His commandments – and die? This doctrine would turn us into self-destructive fools!

I declare to you today, men and brothers, as Moses declared to all Israel in the beginning, that "I am setting before you today a blessing and a curse: the blessing if you obey the commandments of the LORD *your* God, and the curse if you do not obey the commandments of the LORD

---

[325] Prov. 1:28–29.

[326] Jer. 7:12.

[327] Jer. 26:4–6.

[328] Ps. 119:126.

[329] Ps. 78:1.

[330] Prov. 3:1.

[331] Prov. 4:2

[332] Prov. 7:2.

your God."[333] And like Moses, "I summon heaven and earth to bear witness against you today, that I have set before you life and death, blessing and cursing."[334] And I beg you, as brothers in the Lord, and as Moses pleaded with our fathers, "Choose life!"[335]

Council members: *Comments.*

Jesus Divides

Silas: Dear brothers, I beg you to hear us! We understand your feelings. We understand how that Paul's gospel might seem wrong to you. I would think as you do, but Jesus opened my eyes to see what God has done in him, and it is wondrous to behold. You brothers are saying, are you not, that if God commanded us to keep the law, and we did it, and then God rewarded us for doing it, how could keeping the law ever become sin?

Micah: Yes. God commanded Israel not to forsake His law for anything in this world.

Silas: But that was only because, at that time, there was nothing in this world holier than the law, Micah, and anyone who forsook it was going downward, toward destruction. Not only was it sin to forsake the law before Messiah came; it was madness! Who in his right mind would want something less than the holiest and best that God had given? But the Son of God is Lord even of the law, Micah; to go to him is to go upward, toward God. Paul is only saying that something greater than the law has come and that God has given us His Spirit as proof of it. Of all that has ever been in the world, Messiah Jesus is alone worthy of greater honor than the law.

You spoke a little while ago of the day Jesus commanded ten lepers to go to the priest to perform the rite for those cleansed of leprosy. And you noted that they were not healed immediately, but only after they started on their journey to the priest. However, you will remember that when one of them, a foreigner, saw that his leprosy was gone, he was so grateful that he forgot about the law, and Jesus' commandment to obey it, and he ran back to Jesus and fell on his face, thanking him. Do you remember that, Micah?

Micah: Yes, of course.

---

[333] Dt. 11:26–28.
[334] Dt. 30:19a.
[335] Dt. 30:19b.

Silas: And do any of you who were there remember what Jesus said to that Samaritan leper who did not keep the law, but returned to thank Jesus for healing him?

Bartholomew: I do. And Jesus did not rebuke him and say, "Why didn't you obey Moses and me?"

Silas: That's right, Bartholomew. Instead, he said, "Were there none found who returned to give glory to God, except this foreigner? Where are the nine?"[336] Consider that, Micah. Jesus was pleased with that Samaritan *for not keeping the law*, and he wondered aloud why the Jews who were healed did not also return to thank him and give God glory.

Council members: *Comments*.

Silas: It was not sin for that Samaritan to honor Jesus above the law, if only for that moment, and Barnabas and Paul are telling the truth when they say the day is coming when God will demand that we no longer divide our hearts between Moses and Jesus, but serve God in the Spirit and not in the flesh.

Hananiah: But that Samaritan certainly went to the priest after he returned to thank Jesus and give honor to our God. He did not forget Jesus command to do so, surely.

Silas: No doubt. But we moved on with Jesus, and did not see him go.

Hananiah: And with so little support from the prophets for this doctrine, and with so much in the prophets contradicting it, how can reasonable men embrace it?

Hillel: Reasonable, righteous men cannot embrace it, Hananiah. This is not the way of righteousness; it is the way heathen philosophers talk – everything based on something a man thinks instead of what God has commanded. We have the law, Silas; we have the prophets; we have our history; we have Jesus' own example. Look at what we have from God! Are we supposed to ignore all that for this new doctrine?

Micah: And if God has uttered a curse on whoever refuses the law and the prophets, does the thought of that not frighten you? I am grieved by all of this, brothers! And I tell you, if what Barnabas and Paul teach is truly the revelation of Messiah Jesus, then Jesus has chosen to exclude me from the light – so far, anyway. And that thought frightens me as much as the other. I am torn. This gospel of yours is tearing my soul apart!

Hilkiah: It will tear every soul apart who loves the law and Messiah Jesus.

---

[336] Lk. 17:17–18.

Jared: Men and brothers, where in this new doctrine is the peace Jesus said he would give us? Where is the joy in it? This new doctrine has destroyed the peace and harmony we once enjoyed! This doctrine has not brought peace to the household of God, but division. Look at us here today! Is *this* what Jesus died for?

Paul: No, but it is what he is living for. It is necessary, brother Jared, that divisions come, so that it might be made manifest who is hearing God's voice and who is not.

Lamech: I am so tired of clever answers to sincere questions, answers which no man of God has ever said, or ever would say.

Council members: *Comments.*

Daniel: Lamech, we were together the day Jesus warned us that he had not come to bring peace, but to bring trouble and division.[337] He knew what lay ahead for us who loved him. And what hatred we have endured!

Council members: *Comments.*

Daniel: God has a time for all things, my friend, and He makes everything beautiful in its time.[338] How blessed is the man who has the faith to say with David, "All my times are in God's hands." As for your torn heart, Micah, let me remind you that Jesus only uses bread that he has broken.[339] God tries our hearts, and when He sees us bound to anything more than to Him, He sends revelation like a sharp knife to cut the cords that bind us, for He is a jealous God.[340] No pruning of the soul is pleasant, but when expertly done, it produces better fruit.

Maschil: But sir, will God divide His own people from one another?

Cleopas: Haven't we who believe been divided from the rest of Israel and become outcasts in our own country for his name sake?

Maschil: (*slowly*) Yes, we certainly have.

Daniel: Jesus said, "I'm the true vine, and my Father is the vinedresser. He takes away every branch in me that doesn't bear fruit, and He prunes every branch that does bear fruit so that it might bear more fruit."[341] So, our choice, as branches on God's Vine, is to be cut on or to be cut off. If we refuse His pruning of unprofitable branches, God will cut us off with them.

---

[337] Lk. 12:51.

[338] Eccl. 3:11.

[339] Thanks to Jospeh H. "Uncle Joe" Murray for this insight.

[340] Ex. 34:1, 11.

[341] Jn. 15:1–2.

Silas: Yes, Jesus said that we will either fall down and be broken upon the Stone which God has laid, or that Stone will fall on us and crush us to pieces."[342]

Joel: I have always understood that parable to be speaking of the difference between believers and non-believers.

Silas: No, Joel. Jesus was speaking of his own house, the household of God. And a few days before he died, Jesus told us another parable which he plainly applied to the kingdom of God. In God's kingdom, he said, there will be ten virgins waiting for the Bridegroom to come, five of them wise and the other five foolish. The wise are the children of God who hear His voice and fall down on the Stone, to be cut on and broken. The foolish are the children of God who resist His will, and when the Stone returns from heaven, he will crush them and cut them off. So, yes, Maschil, God will divide His own people. He has done so many times, throughout our history.

Daniel: Know this, son, and prepare your heart: if you serve God well, as I believe you will, God will prune you so that you may serve Him better. And if you do not serve Him according to His will, He will certainly cut you off from the Vine. No man is ever so holy or wise that God cannot make him holier and wiser, but that God will do so only to the man who humbles himself to be cut on and broken. For us, to be increasingly like the Son of God is the greatest blessing in life, and that blessing will be an eternal one, for God will never cease either from increasing His Son's glory or from making us more like him.

Council members: *Comments.*

A New Nation

Jared: Brother Paul, I would ask you something.

Paul: Of course.

Jared: You say that the Gentiles who believe, yet are not circumcised, are fellow-citizens with us in a new Israel.

Paul: Yes. We are all one in the family of God, circumcised in heart by the Spirit.

Jared: . . . even though Jesus called the Gentiles dogs?

---

[342] Lk. 20:18.

Paul: But what were *we*? Do I need to recount the ways God has described Israel at times? "Stiff-necked",[343] Not-my-people",[344] "Sodom",[345] and a hundred more such titles?

Bartholomew: I would rather Jesus call me a dog and then answer my prayer, as he did that Phoenician woman,[346] than to call me a stiff-necked sodomite. What's so bad about being a dog? Just bark and roll over, and let Jesus feed you.

Paul: Whatever any of us were in the past means nothing now if God has forgiven and cleansed us.

Lamech: Jesus did not feel the kinship with the heathen that you do, Paul.

Simon Peter: We all should feel kinship with anyone Jesus has loved. God told me before sending me to the house of Cornelius not to condemn any man if He has cleansed him.

Hillel: We do not condemn the Gentiles who believe, but we certainly warn them that *God* will condemn them if they do not obey His law. The God that met with Moses on Mount Sinai said, "I am the LORD thy God; I change not!" So, let the Gentiles change and be circumcised so that there be no division!

Lamech, Hushai, Nadab, Hilkiah, Eli: *Amen!*

Paul: That circumcision is in the flesh, Hillel, and it will perish with your flesh. Messiah ministers an eternal circumcision by the Spirit of God.

Eli: When did God ever say that His covenant of circumcision with father Abraham was temporary? If God has not said it, I will not believe it.

Paul: You know the promise Moses made when he was about to die: "The LORD your God will circumcise your heart, and the heart of your seed, to love the LORD your God with all your heart, and with all your soul, that you may live."[347]

Eli: Moses was saying that God would circumcise the hearts *of His circumcised people,* not the heathen! And God has done so, for the Spirit has now circumcised the hearts of many in Israel, and every one of them, just as Jacobus said earlier, is zealous for the law.[348]

---

[343] Ex. 32:9.

[344] Hos. 1:9.

[345] Isa. 1:9–10.

[346] Mk. 7:25–30.

[347] Dt. 30:6.

[348] Acts 21:20.

Paul: And they should be, for they are Jews.

Eli: It is impossible to get a straight answer from you!

Double Meanings

Paul: That *was* a straight answer, Eli. Listen, I was as devoted to the law as any man here, and I thought as you do now, that the law would remain forever the way into eternal life. But Jesus changed that. *He* is our life now – by God's decree, not by the law of carnal commandments. That law is behind us, as glorious as it once was, and the Spirit is not leading Gentiles to it. And soon, the Spirit will lead believing Jews completely out of it!

Philip: Why would we even want to yoke the believing Gentiles to our law? They believe, and it is enough. Let us bear our own burden.

Paul: More than that, why would we seek to convert the converted? The Gentiles who believe are Jews already in God's eyes, citizens with us in the new Israel of God.

Council members: *Comments.*

Paul: Hosea once said of the Gentiles, "In the place where it was said to them, 'You are not my people,' it shall be said to them, 'You are sons of the living God.'"[349] That was God's promise to the Gentiles. And in that promise, God spoke nothing of circumcision or the law, for God is a judge of the heart, and where He finds a humble, obedient heart, there He will be!

Nadab: Are you saying that God will choose sinners of the Gentiles instead of His own people?

Paul: Did God not warn Israel He would do that when He commanded Hosea to name his son, "Not-My-People"? God told Israel that He gave that name to Hosea's child "because *you* are not my people, and I will not be *your* God."[350]

Hushai: Aha! You have completely misrepresented Hosea's words, Paul. Anyone who has read Hosea knows that God was speaking of *Israel* no longer being called His people, and then returning to Israel after He had called them, "Not-My-People". God was not speaking of the heathen or of calling them instead of us. You are found out!

Paul: I wish I was truly found out, Hushai. It is hard, having a vision that others cannot see. Many times, as was said earlier, the prophets' words had double meanings, coming as they did from the wisdom of God.

---

[349] Hos. 1:10.

[350] Hos. 1:8–9.

Hillel said earlier that I misrepresented what Jeremiah said about all men being brutish in knowledge, but I did not. I was showing him God's hidden meaning in those words, just as I was showing His hidden meaning to you in Hosea.

Hushai: Hidden meanings are a matter of opinion, Paul, and clever men can see a multitude of them.

Paul: Then see this, you clever man. When Isaiah prophesied of the Babylonians invading our land with their foreign language,[351] he thought he was prophesying only of Nebuchadnezzar's invasion of this land. But by the unfathomable wisdom of God, he was also prophesying of the Son's outpouring of the Spirit, which moves us to speak in languages foreign to ourselves when it enters our temples. What difference does it make what Isaiah thought he was saying? It was God doing the talking, and He knew what His Son would do.

Council members: Comments

Paul: Yes, Hushai, the prophet Hosea no doubt thought God was speaking only about Israel being put away and then reunited with Him. But what was on God's mind? The Son came to let us know what his Father was thinking, and that is what I was revealing to you. I wish you men could see it the way Jesus showed it to me.

Silas: We can only sow the seed, Paul; God chooses which seed to water.

Hushai: Keep your seed and your water! I want no part of it.

Council members: *Comments.*

A New Standard

Micah: Barnabas, my friend, this division between us is painful. You know me. You know that if I believed God wanted me to cease from the law, I would cease from it this moment.

Barnabas: Yes, Micah, I believe you would, and so would I. But the time to do that has not come. However, when it comes, it will be sin for us not to leave the law behind.

Silas: And God forewarned us of that time, Micah, when He said in Isaiah, "Slaughtering one of the herd will be like killing a man; sacrificing one of the flock, like breaking a dog's neck; offering up a gift, like offering up blood from a pig; burning incense, like blessing an idol."[352]

Council members: *Comments.*

---

[351] Isa. 28:11–12.

[352] Isa. 66:3.

Micah: So, you interpret Isaiah to mean it will someday be sinful to perform the holy rites?

Barnabas: How else could it be interpreted?

Maschil: God many times condemned those who performed the law's ceremonies while transgressing His moral commandments. We know that. It has always been sinful for the wicked to perform the law's holy rites.

Silas: That is true, Maschil, but in this case, Isaiah was speaking of a time when God would no longer accept such worship from anyone, for he went on in that same prophecy to foretell of *our* time, when God would create a new nation of saints by the Spirit coming from His temple in heaven with the sound of a storm-wind. He said, "A sound from the temple! Who has heard such a thing? Who has seen such things? Shall the earth be born in one day? Shall a nation be born at once?"[353] Jesus has founded a new nation; he is our new father Abraham! Our new Adam, the first of a new race of men!

Council members: *Comments.*

Paul: It is not those who have inherited Abraham's kind of flesh who are God's children, but those who possess Abraham's kind of faith, whatever nation they are from. In Messiah Jesus, neither circumcision nor uncircumcision means anything, but having God's life does! God is not looking for circumcision, brothers; He is looking for faith in His Son. He looks at the heart of man, not his flesh!

Council members: *Comments.*

Paul: Didn't John the Baptist say as much when he rebuked the hypocrites who came from Jerusalem to be baptized by him? Didn't he tell them not to justify themselves by saying that Abraham was their father, for God was able to raise up children to Abraham from stones if He chose to?[354]

Lamech: Unlike you, Paul, I actually heard John preach, and he never said that *any* man of *any* nation who believes in Messiah Jesus is free from the law. John himself kept it!

Hushai, Hillel, Nadab, Eli, Hilkiah: *Amen! That's right. Etc.*

Barnabas: But if John had not kept it, none of you would have believed him and repented at his preaching.

Hillel: Oh, spare us, Barnabas! The next thing you will say is that King David kept the law just so the people would accept him as Israel's King.

---

[353] Isa. 66:6, 8.

[354] Mt. 3:9; Lk. 3:8.

Paul: No, David kept the law because it was of God and he loved it, just as Moses and all the prophets loved it.

Eli: So did Jesus! My! How you can twist things!

Paul: I am twisting nothing. Messiah has made the righteousness of God, not our righteousness, the new standard. Keeping Moses' law no longer makes men righteous in God's sight; in fact, to keep it will soon be rebellion against Him. God's eyes are now on His Son – and not His Son as a Jew, but His Son as the one by whom He made the worlds. No one comes to God but by him, and without him, all men are in bondage to their own thoughts and ways, whether keeping the law or not.

Eli: We are not walking in our own thoughts and ways if we are keeping God's law. We are righteous if we walk in God's law.

Paul: In this covenant, Jesus alone makes men righteous in God's sight. Moses' law is no longer the standard of righteousness! Those who trust the law to keep them sinless should heed the warning of God through Jeremiah: "Behold, I will plead my case against you for saying, 'I have not sinned.'"[355] I tell you that all have sinned, Jew and Gentile alike, and all have fallen short of God's righteousness.

Lamech: Then you are saying that God's holy law is not perfect because those who keep it are still sinners.

Paul: God found fault with His people, not with His law.

Lamech: Bah!

Hananiah: It will be a difficult task, Paul, for you to persuade Israel that God will call on us to cease from the law that He gave us. Our hearts know no other way to love Him but to keep His law.

Paul: Yes, we know that. And God knows that. That is why He does not require our nation to cease immediately from it. But, Hananiah, God will not call upon all of Israel to do that, but only those of us who have obeyed His call to believe in His Son. We are the ones whose conscience the Spirit will purge from the law's works, so that we may be free from fear of living without them. The rest of Israel, those who have rejected Messiah Jesus, will be cursed with the law, to live and to worship their own way instead of God's way.

Council members: *Comments.*

Hananiah: To bring about such a change in Israel's conscience will take a mighty work of the Spirit, Paul.

Barnabas: Yes, but then, it takes the power of the Spirit to do anything rightly in this covenant, doesn't it?

Hananiah: I understand what you are saying.

---

[355] Jer. 2:35.

Others Walk Out

Lamech: I also understand what Barnabas and Paul are saying; that is why I oppose it. Hananiah, are you and Micah falling under the spell of these men? How can keeping the law with a pure heart ever be wrong?

Paul: When God finishes with the law, no pure heart *will* keep it. All the righteous in every place will trust in Messiah alone to save them, and he is able. To refuse His grace and continue in Moses' handwritten law will lead to death, but God's Spirit sanctifies us and gives us life.

Lamech: Nothing that is truly from God would lead men away from His law.

Hillel: Your doctrine, Paul, puts God's people in a position of having to choose between you and the Jesus with whom we walked.

Micah: How do you answer that, Paul? It seems that for you to teach that God will, at whatever point in time, make it sinful to walk by the law that He gave us would make Jesus sinful. And I hesitate to say it, but it makes you seem evil, too.

Paul: No need for you to hesitate, Micah. I know your heart. And I know how my gospel sounds to you and to many other of my countrymen. But I am content with being a sheep in wolf's clothing.[356] The truth often appears to be an enemy until we learn the mind of the Father. On the other hand, the Deceiver has often disguised his deceit and appeared to be good by using something God did or said in the past. You remember that God allowed Abraham to build an altar under a grove.

Micah: Yes, in Beersheba.[357]

Paul: But in later generations, after God had forbidden groves to be planted near His altar,[358] false prophets justified their continued worship under groves by proclaiming, "The manner of Beersheba lives,"[359] because Abraham had worshipped there. But they lied. The manner of Beersheba was dead. God had changed the acceptable place of worship to His temple.

Micah: I see that, yes.

Paul: And in not too long a time, this will be the same. Jesus kept the law, but when God finishes with it, false teachers will again rise up, but

---

[356] Thanks to my father, George C. "Preacher" Clark, for this and several other witticisms in this work.

[357] Gen. 21:33.

[358] Dt. 16:21.

[359] Amos 8:14.

this time proclaiming, "The manner of the law lives because Jesus kept it," instead of "the manner of Beersheba lives because Abraham kept it."

Lamech: This is blasphemous!

Paul: Was Isaiah blaspheming when he said that making sacrifices according to the law will one day be all the same as cutting a dog's neck?

Council members: *Comments.*

Paul: Brother Lamech, I understand the concerns that you and your companions have, being shepherds of the flock of God, and I confess that when Messiah took me into the third heaven, I heard things unlawful to be said. But . . .

Lamech: So, Paul, you finally admit that your revelation teaches what the law condemns! You admit that you are a false prophet!

Paul: False prophets were considered false only because they led God's people away from the holiest thing God had given at the time, the law. But now, something holier than the law has come, and we are not leading men *away from* the holiest thing, but *to* it: the Son of the living God.

When the Spirit came, Lamech, it changed everything, and yet, God has given us Jews a little season to adjust to this new thing and to prepare our hearts to walk in the newness of His life. If you refuse the light, and choose rather to continue in the flesh, you will die. But if you live in the Spirit, you will live forever. Whoever worships God in the Spirit of truth, anywhere on this earth, worships God well. God has not merely chosen a new place for worship; He has created a new way to worship, fulfilling His purpose for the law and bringing it to its intended end.

Council members: *Comments.*

Hushai: [*calmly*] An intended end for an eternal law. If that is not a heathen philosophical concept, meant only to provoke debate and promote oneself, such a thing does not exist.

Council members: *Comments.*

Hushai: I congratulate you, Paul, you and Barnabas. Really, I do. This new doctrine of yours is very tightly woven. Almost impossible to unravel. Without a firm grasp of the law and a deep love for Messiah Jesus, with whom I walked when I could, I don't know that any man could successfully resist you. Look at the men in this room whom you have already taken in! And I know you can sense that you are about to take in a few more, who at the start of this meeting were determined to be faithful to God and His law. I really do congratulate you; few men could ever have accomplished what you and Barnabas have accomplished here.

Paul: Wrangling over these things will never reveal the mind of the Spirit to you, Hushai. Either the knowledge of God is revealed to a man, or it is never comprehended. Even with the Spirit, we understand nothing if the Spirit reveals nothing, for nothing of God is understood without the Spirit's aid, whether we have it or not. I can testify to what I have received, but I cannot open your heart to receive it; that is the work of God. He wrought that work on me when He sent Jesus to arrest me on the road to Damascus – Jesus, who alone knows the Father and who has revealed the Father to me. And I praise him for it! I rejoice in his light!

Simon Peter: I join you, Paul!

[Some] Council members: *Amen! Praise God! Etc.*

Eli: Go ahead, brothers! Go ahead and rejoice in darkness with these men if you like. Be carried away with their revelations and their exploits among the heathen. "Mighty works," they say – and so they may have been – but God warned Israel to refuse the man who would lead us away from His law, *even if that man performed miracles!*[360]

Council members: *Comments.*

Eli: And what did God say to do with such a man, brothers?

Hananiah: Eli, wait . . . .

Eli: Wait for what? For this Council to take a vote on what God said? I did not come here for men to decide on what God said any more than Paul came here for men to decide on what he says. Every one of you knows that God commanded the judges to put such a man to death, not just to refuse his doctrine, "for he has spoken apostasy against the LORD *y*our God, the One who brought *y*ou out from the land of Egypt and re-deemed you from the house of bondage, to thrust you out from the way that the LORD your God commanded you to walk in."[361]

Why so silent, brothers? No stomach for the law of your God? When the rulers brought to Jesus that woman caught in adultery, did Jesus tell them not to stone her? No! He agreed with the law that she was worthy of death, and he told them to stone her! He only said that the appropriate men should do it, which was also according to the law. The fact that those rulers were wicked and could not stone her does not mean that Jesus thought the law was wrong and that she should not be stoned. He may have been waiting for you righteous disciples to stone her, instead of those fools, but you did not! Why?

Jacobus: Would you have wanted to stone her, Eli?

---

[360] Dt. 13:1–4.
[361] Dt. 13:5.

Eli: What I want means nothing. God's will is what matters, and God commanded such a woman to be stoned.

False doctrine always, sooner or later, forces God's people to this crossroads, where we stand today: should we do God's will, or should we do our own will, as in the days of the judges, when "every man did what was right in his own eyes."[362] But what did God's servant Moses command Israel when they were in the wilderness? Or does it any longer even matter to you what Moses said?

Hillel, Lamech, Hilkiah, Hushai, Nadab: *It matters to me. Moses was right. Etc.*

Eli: Moses said, "You shall not do as all of us are doing here, today, each man doing whatever is right in his own eyes."[363]

Jacobus: Eli, Jesus has given us no authority to punish the wicked.

Lamech: He most certainly has! He told some of the leaders of our nation that his disciples would be their judges[364] and that they would sit on thrones, judging the twelve tribes![365] Forgetting the law is even making you men forget the words of Messiah Jesus! What has happened here? At the very least, you should be able agree that what *Jesus* said was of God and that it revealed what God thinks we who follow Jesus should do to those who would turn our nation from the law.

Council members: *Comments.*

Joseph: To execute judgments on sinners is not the way of Jesus, Lamech. Jesus was no more sent to be a judge on earth than he was sent to be a priest on earth.

Eli: If it is not the way of Jesus, then tell me what the prophets meant when they said of Messiah, "He will smite the earth with the rod of his mouth, and with the breath of his lips will he slay the wicked"?[366]

Andrew: Jesus will do that when he returns, Eli, when he returns. He said, "When the Son of man sits down on his glorious throne, *you* who have followed me will sit on twelve thrones, judging the twelve tribes of Israel."[367]

Lamech: And until then, we are to do nothing in the face of evil, Andrew? Did Jesus not tell us to "take care of things until I come"?[368]

---

[362] Judg. 17:6; 21:25.

[363] Dt. 12:8.

[364] Mt. 12:24–27; Lk. 11:15–19.

[365] Mt. 19:28b; Lk. 22:29–30.

[366] Isa. 11:4b.

[367] Mt. 19:28.

[368] Lk. 19:13.

Eli's point, harsh though it sounds, is in perfect accord with what God commanded Moses. Did not God command the judges to destroy those who lead Israel away from the law?

Paul: [*resignedly*] Yes. Yes, He did, Lamech.

Lamech: And if your doctrine takes root in the Assemblies in Judah, you would eventually lead thousands of Jews away from the law!

Paul: Not I, but Jesus. We are just following his lead in this new covenant.

Council members: *Comments.*

Lamech: Has God ever made an old covenant? Every time God has ever made a covenant, it was new when He made it. The law itself was the new covenant when God first gave it. When answers are not answers, Paul, they are bait for more debate. Your answers are not answers.

Council members: *Comments.*

Lamech: You seem to have won an impressive following with your craftiness, Paul, even some of Jesus' own disciples! The glory you enjoyed among the wicked priests and elders while persecuting us pales in comparison to the glory you and Barnabas now have among the heathen. How many Gentiles now follow you instead of Moses and the law?

Silas: Lamech, that is enough.

Eli: Do we not have good reason to be suspicious of you, Paul of Tarsus? Some say that since you failed to destroy the faith from the outside . . .

Lamech: He seized my brother and dragged him before the Sanhedrin!

Eli: . . . you are now trying to destroy it from the inside with this new religion of yours!

Jacobus, Apostles, and others: *Stop! That is not right! Etc.*

Barnabas: I will answer that. Brother Paul has risked his life for the name of Jesus. I have seen him endure suffering for the name of the Lord in as great a measure as he ever inflicted it on others. He has proved his love for all the saints to be greater than the hatred he once bore toward us. He has suffered hunger and thirst; he has been cursed by men, jailed, beaten and left for dead, slandered and despised, and yet he has borne all things with humility and patience.

Paul: Brothers, in none of those things do I boast. I am worthy of worse suffering than any that I have endured. I am the least of all the saints, and am not worthy to be an apostle. Still, by the grace of God, I am what I am.

Micah: Barnabas and Paul, I apologize for my companions' fervor, but your doctrine stirs up strong passions among those who are devoted to the law. You must be able to see why we cannot accept your new revelation. It is a danger to the well-being of the Assemblies of God, whom we love. Your new revelation is outside the flow of our history; it is not consonant with the law and the prophets.

Hillel: Amen, Micah. "The legs of a lame man are unequal; so is a parable in the mouth of fools."[369]

Paul: Though we be fools, if you would listen, you would become wise.

Council members: *Comments.*

Paul: What else is there to be said, brothers? All that remains is for us who belong to the Lord to prepare ourselves for the changes that God will make, lest we stumble at the stumbling block which God has laid for this people: Messiah Jesus. He is a sanctuary for the humble, but for those among us who resist God's will, he will be "a stumbling-stone, a trap and a snare, and many of them will stumble, and fall, and be broken, and be snared and taken."[370] When that happens, the door for the Jews to enter the kingdom of God will be closed for a time, and the truth will be found only among those who have listened to His voice, as Messiah said again through Isaiah, "Bind up the testimony! Seal the law among those who are taught by me! And I will wait for the LORD, who is hiding His face from the house of Jacob."[371]

Eli: We are not resisting the Lord Jesus, Paul! We are resisting you!

Paul: Prepare yourselves, I say! God will not long tolerate two gospels of His one Son.

Lamech: There *already* are not two gospels, for yours is no gospel at all!

Paul: There *is* a gospel for the uncircumcision, and the day is coming when the gospel I preach will be the only gospel recognized by heaven.

Council members: *Comments.*

Barnabas: Listen to Paul, brothers! God destroyed Jerusalem in the days of Nebuchadnezzar because the people refused to hear His prophets. Do you think He will not use the Romans to do the same if you refuse the truth? And when God does that, brothers, when He destroys this holy city again, how will you explain that to your children? Whom will you blame!

---

[369] Prov. 26:7.

[370] Isa. 8:14–15.

[371] Isa. 8:16–17a.

Hillel: You prophesy to us? No! You hear my prophecy, Barnabas, and all of you! If and when Jerusalem's destruction comes about – and it must come, for Jesus said it will – it will come because this people forsake God's law and do not reject false teaching. That has always been the source of Israel's troubles. So, when that dreadful destruction comes, it will come because Barnabas and Paul's doctrine is accepted by this people, as most of you seem to have already done!

Nathan: God would have spared even Sodom if he had found but ten righteous souls in that city.[372] Surely, there is hope that He will not destroy the city where He has poured out His Spirit upon thousands!

Paul: That is what the false prophets also taught, Nathan, that God will not destroy this city because His temple is here.[373] Take heed that you don't become like them. If those thousands of Jews who believe continue to follow Jesus, they will learn the truth, just as he promised,[374] and they will be spared. Otherwise, they will be cut off with the city.

John: Hillel! Nathan! Brothers! Paul is telling the truth. It grieves me, too, but the truth is the truth, and just men choose to see the truth and suffer, rather than deny it in order to avoid the pain. Jesus also saw it and grieved deeply over it. The last time he came here, when he saw the city from the hill across the Kidron, he broke down and wept, and cried out, "O Jerusalem! If only you had known the things which lead to your peace! But now, they are hidden from your eyes, and the days shall come upon you when enemies will raze you to the ground because you did not recognize the time of your visitation!"[375]

Hillel: But it will be the fault of these men, John! This blindness is maddening!

And as for you, Paul and Barnabas, I say there will be a great reward from heaven for the men who trace your footsteps in every city where you have preached, and repair the damage you have done to those ignorant Gentiles whom God has called! Father Jacob said that God's Messiah would be the Lawgiver,[376] but you men would make him the Law-taker instead. We cannot accede to this doctrine of yours; it is contrary not only to the law and the prophets, but also to the Spirit of God. Without obeying the law, even Messiah Jesus would have been unrighteous, but you say anyone can be righteous without it.

---

[372] Gen. 18:23–32.

[373] Cf. Jer. 7:4.

[374] Jn. 8:31–32.

[375] Excerpts, Lk. 19:41–44.

[376] Gen. 49:10.

Council members: *Comments.*

Paul: I beg you to hear me. My gospel was given to me by Jesus. I did not expect it any more than you did.

Barnabas: We are telling the truth.

Hushai: Then there are two truths, Barnabas, and one is contrary to the other! And that cannot be, unless – God forgive me for saying it! – there are two Gods! Paul, recover yourself from this madness!

Paul: This is not madness, Hushai, unless Jesus is mad, for he revealed it to me.

Hananiah: I am utterly speechless at this . . . this teaching.

Lamech: Paul, your father was a Roman, was he not?

Paul: A Roman citizen, yes.

Lamech: And through him, you no doubt became more acquainted with the ways of the heathen than, say, a Jewish child living here in this land.

Paul: I adhered to the strictest sect of the Pharisees from my youth. I was a Pharisee, like you, with zeal similar to yours for the traditions of our fathers.

Lamech: Yes, we are aware of your great devotion to the law as a young man sitting at the feet of Gamaliel.[377] But your doctrine certainly didn't come from him. Might it not be that your father's heathen associations introduced you, however inadvertently, to the Gentiles' philosophic frame of mind?

Paul: I have told you, I did not receive this doctrine from man. It came by revelation from Messiah Jesus.

Lamech: I know, I know. I heard you. But how many times, when my colleagues exposed you as being in error, instead of reasoning with them, you resorted to "Messiah told me", and then proceeded to say things no one has ever said, even Jesus! Does that sound reasonable to you? Who can reason with a man whose principal response is to claim private revelations and to say things that no one has ever heard? I know, men and brothers, that revelation is necessary. I thank God for it. But God is the One who called us to reason together; therefore, there must be a time and place for reason, too.

Let us not forget the man of God whom God sent to Bethel to condemn the king's idolatry there. God straitly commanded that prophet to return to Judah immediately after delivering His message and to stop nowhere in the apostate north. After he prophesied at Bethel, the king in the north invited him to his palace to be refreshed and to receive money

---

[377] Acts 22:3.

for his labor, but he told the king, "Even if you give me half your house, I will not come with you, nor will I eat bread or drink water in this place. For thus it was commanded me by the word of the LORD, saying, 'You shall not eat bread nor drink water in the north, nor shall you return by the same road by which you came.'"

And yet that good man, so determined, at first, to obey the commandment of God, like brother Paul in his youth, proved to be a fool. For an old false prophet in Bethel heard news of him, and he caught up with him, and deceived him, and persuaded him to come to his house rather than to continue on his journey home! And how did that false prophet persuade him, but by claiming that he had received a new revelation from God and that God had changed His will for that man of God?378 The man of God knew what God had commanded him, but he trusted that old man's "new revelation" instead of obeying what he knew had come from God, and died for his foolishness.

Council members: *Comments.*

Lamech: Now, brothers, hear me! Barnabas and Paul are not the only men to have arisen in Israel, declaring new things contrary to what we all know God commanded. And they are not the only men to have interpreted scriptures in novel ways in order to gain a following. If any of us has wondered how Israel could have been fooled so often in the past, after knowing of God's judgment on those who were lured away from His law, this is your chance to learn. This is how it happened. This is what false teachers sound like; they are very convincing and very insistent that you trust them and their new revelation instead of trusting what you know is from God.

That said, I will take my leave now of this Council and this Assembly, for there is no room here for the things I believe, and I will not hear any more of this quibbling over the simple truth of God. [*Lamech leaves.*]

Jacobus, John, Silas and others: *No, Lamech! Lamech, don't go. Stay, brother Lamech. Etc.*

Paul: [*after Lamech is gone*] That man speaks pretty well to be as wrong as he is.

Maschil: How can such plain truth be wrong?

Paul: It isn't the way it appears, Maschil. That old false prophet from Bethel who deceived the man of God was false because he claimed that God had spoken to him when He had not. The man of God should not have listened to him. And if Messiah Jesus has not spoken to me, I am false, too, as false as Lamech thinks I am, and you should not listen to me,

---

378 1Kgs. 13:1–32.

either. But Jesus *has* spoken to me, and because that is true, you *should* listen to me because the words I speak are not mine, but his, and they are judging you; you are not judging them. You can't. And neither can any other man.

Council members: *Comments.*

Hilkiah: Brothers, none of us think Barnabas and Paul are liars. Lies spring from evil hearts with wicked intent, and no such person is present in this Council. However, lies can be passed on unawares by men of good intent when they are persuaded to believe them, and I believe that is what is happening here. Our Enemy knows that his lies have their greatest effect when otherwise good men are persuaded of them and, in their undiscerning sincerity, pass his lies on for him. The most effective liars, then, are righteous men when they are wrongly persuaded that they are speaking the truth.

Now, it may be that Barnabas and Paul have had some kind of spiritual experience which they truly believe was with the Lord Jesus. He loved and obeyed the law and taught others to do the same, and that is the testimony of many of you here today, but in spite of that, it seems that you are persuaded by Barnabas and Paul that their testimony is better, for you now argue with them against your own experience with the Lord Jesus.

Brothers, God truly is testing us, and it is our place to uphold the law of our God and show them again the way, for they have wandered off the right path, and they need us. Jesus will be our judge, brothers, and when we stand before him, what shall we say if we have forsaken the path he walked and have followed other men who claim to have a new revelation from him?

Paul: You are right about one thing, Hilkiah; I am fully persuaded of my gospel, but not wrongly, for I learned it neither from man nor from lying spirit, but from Jesus. He is our salvation, and nothing else. Continuing in the law after God's Son has come leaves the false impression that God has not made Jesus the only Savior but that he needs help from Moses to save us. *That* is the lie, Hilkiah, and you are the one who is telling it, thinking to do good. Didn't Jesus say that the time would come when men would kill his servants, thinking to do God service?[379] The men who walked out of here would condone the killing of anyone who believes my gospel and trusts in Jesus alone to save them. They left here determined to do what God sees as evil, but what they think is good, and you and others would help them. But I am warning all of you that my gospel reveals God's heart and, by excluding the works of Moses' law, my

---

[379] Jn. 16:2.

gospel reveals God's Son Jesus to be man's only hope of salvation, not Jesus *and* the law!

Council members: *Comments.*

Daniel: Hilkiah, what you said about good people unwittingly spreading false information is like the use of logic; it is true only when speaking of man's kind of life. Men are weak-hearted creatures, even good men, and are often persuaded of things that are not true. And then they do exactly as you said. But the Spirit of God is not like that; it never tells a lie, nor does it ever believe one. And when we walk in it, we never believe a lie and, so, never unwittingly pass on a lie to others. No one could lie to Jesus because there was no lie in him; he walked in the Spirit of truth. And any man who follows his example and stays full of the Spirit cannot spread lies, any more than the sun can spread darkness.

Hilkiah: But every man here has been filled with the Spirit, brother Daniel, and look at this division!

Daniel: That is why I said that no one who *stays* filled with the Spirit will take in a lie. To receive the Spirit is one thing; to walk in the Spirit is another. Many have received the Spirit and then returned to their old ways; God has always had some foolish children. Think of Ananias and Sapphira; you saw them drop dead, Hilkiah, just after you were converted.

Eli: All this is beside the point, Brother Daniel. Paul says he loves the law, and yet, he teaches salvation without it! He is an apostate!

Paul: I am not an apostate, Eli. Why should the Gentiles keep the law? For whom would they be doing so? Their fellow Gentiles, to whom the law is unknown? No! I will tell you who they would be keeping the law for – you! – so that you can boast about how many converts you have made, when in truth, you will have only made a name for yourself and robbed God of His glory!

Eli: Rob God of His glory by obeying His command to keep the law? Absurd!

Paul: God warned us through Malachi that He would smear the law like dung on your faces, once He is finished with it, saying, "I will smear offal on *your* faces, the offal of *your* festival sacrifices, and one will lift up *your* faces to it"[380]

Eli: Do you hear this, brothers? Paul, you truly have gone mad!

Paul: I am not mad. This is the word of the Lord in my mouth to you, brother! To every one of you! Nothing is holy unless God is in it, and when He moves out of a thing, as He once moved out of the high places, that thing becomes worthless as dung for salvation. And I am telling you

---

[380] Mal. 2:3.

that the law, with all its holy ceremonies, and Jerusalem itself, will become as dung when God finishes with them, and it will not be long.

Council members: *Comments.*

Paul: Beware – all of you! – that God does not smear that dung on your faces!

Eli: Your gospel is dung, Paul of Tarsus, and I will have none of it on my face or in my heart! We have no fear of your vain threats. Your gospel is a stench to the righteous.

Paul: If the truth offend, let it offend! According to you, Barnabas and I are reprobates, but not according to God.

Jared: [*Jared rises.*] Men and brothers, I have, for the most part, avoided engaging in this ungodly verbal sparring, and in my judgment, it has produced nothing worthy of the name of Jesus. For some time now, I have watched with amazement as men who were once my guides, and with whom I joyously labored in the faith of Jesus, were seduced to forsake the way of the Lord. I listened carefully to a number of your conversations previous to this Council concerning this new gospel, and the blindness of your hearts grieved mine. But I held my peace, to see what would come of it. And now, I see.

In this Council, I have listened rather than speak because the wisdom of God has taught me not to argue with foolish men, lest I become like them.[381] Moreover, the truth is never vindicated, as Uzziel said, when we reason with men who will not hear the law, the fountain of truth on earth. We demean God's truth by debating about it. One wondrous quality of the truth is that it refuses to be the subject of debate; it vanishes from strife like smoke in the wind and leaves the debaters quibbling over two wrong ways.

"To the law and to the testimony" was not a clever phrase invented by man; it was God's command through His prophet, and the word of God is entirely non-negotiable – at least, in the hearts of the wise. This Council should have reproved Barnabas and Paul at the outset for denying that holy command of our God, much less for all their other follies; instead, you joined them in that folly, and I fear for what may lie ahead for us all because of it.

As for me, I have concluded that I will – I must – labor as I can to save Israel from this new doctrine, with its lofty phrases and claims of authority. It is manifestly not the way of God; Jesus knew nothing of it. Who will come with me to find Uzziel and join him in upholding the true standard of God?

---

[381] Prov. 26:4.

Hillel: I will, but let me say this before we leave. The whole matter comes down to this: are we to believe God or Barnabas and Paul? Do we believe that God's judgments are everlasting, as God said a hundred times, or do we believe these men, who say they are not? Lamech was right. It is foolish even to ask such a question. But that is the degradation to which this doctrine has brought us.

Paul: Barnabas and I are doing nothing but what Moses and the prophets foretold. And though we love you all, I consider the revelation of Jesus to be more precious than my life, and I will yield it to no man! No, not for one hour!

Hillel: Then yield to Jesus! He straitly commanded us not to go to the Gentiles!

Paul: Then don't *you* go to them! But he did not forbid *me*!

Hillel: We would forbid nothing if you would tell the Gentiles the truth!

Paul: If I preached your gospel to the Gentiles, I would be lying to them!

Hushai: Then God sent Peter to Cornelius' house to preach a lie?

Paul: God sent Peter there to preach the gospel, and God decided that day what the gospel would be, not Peter who preached it, and I believe every word Peter preached. You are the one who would condemn God and change it! You taught false doctrine to the Gentiles in Antioch by saying to them what Peter had planned to say to Cornelius, but God interrupted him, and I interrupted you. Peter now thanks God for stopping him, Hushai. And when your heart is purged from your pride, you will thank me for stopping you.

Nadab: Jesus preached our gospel.

Paul: You fool. Have you learned nothing? Jesus preached what he preached because God sent him to the Jews. God forbade him to go to the Gentiles.

Barnabas: And it was not because God hated the Gentiles that He forbade Messiah to go to them. He sent him to us first in order to fulfill His promises to our fathers, whom He loved. From the foundation of the world, God planned to call the Gentiles, but to call them *by our gospel*, not yours.

Hushai: There is one gospel, Barnabas, and it is true at all times and in all places! And we will go with it to the Gentiles, with this Council's approval or not, and we will save them by doing so!

Barnabas: Hushai!   Do you think that God was like an impatient child at Cornelius' house, that He baptized them with His Spirit on credit, expecting them to become Jews or be damned in the Judgment?

Paul: The gospel you preach, Hushai, justifies both Israel and God because it demands both the law and the Spirit.   That is why you love it so.   But that will cease, and God alone will be glorified – by *our* gospel, not yours!

Messiah prayed through David that God would avenge him of those in this nation who would not forsake the works of the law to walk with him in the Spirit.   He prayed that God would turn those works, given to Israel for a blessing, into a curse for those who would not acknowledge my gospel, saying, "Let their table be a snare before them, and the things they are content with, a trap."[382]

Hillel: Men and brothers!   Messiah was not speaking through David about Paul!

Paul: No, he was speaking through David about you and all others who would cling to a dead thing when the Son of God has brought us life. That is my gospel, and it glorifies nobody but God and His Son!

Council members: *Comments.*

Hillel: I am going to serve God the way that Messiah Jesus served God!   We will answer to God, not to you, Paul, for the path we choose. "As for me and my house, we will serve the Lord!"[383]   "I took an oath, and I will perform it, to keep His righteous judgments."[384]   And though I am troubled by this Council's refusal to hear us, I will not fear man, for God said, "Hear me, *you* people in whose heart is my law! Do not fear the reproach of man, for the moth shall eat them like a garment, and the worm shall eat them like wool."[385]

This new doctrine will bring God's wrath on you who are taken in by it.   Beware, you who are wavering!   "He will come like an eagle against the house of the LORD because they have rebelled against my law."[386] Hear the word of the Lord, O men of God, who are seduced by strange men who have turned you from my word!   "Behold, I will bring evil on this people because they have not attended to my words, and they have rejected my law."[387]

---

[382] Ps. 69:22.

[383] Josh. 24:15b.

[384] Ps. 119:106.

[385] Isa. 51:7–8.

[386] Hos. 8:1.

[387] Jer. 6:19.

If you do not heed that voice, my brothers, you will not heed anything that I have to say. Come, Jared. I am ready to leave now. [*Hillel leaves with Jared.*]

Council members: *Hillel! Brother Jared! Come back. Etc.*

Hushai: My God, did no one here feel the authority in what Hillel was saying? Do you men really not see what God is saying to you?

John: I can see that Jesus is well able to cleanse a soul and save it without help from Moses.

Andrew: . . . and Paul's gospel makes that truth perfectly clear, Hushai, whereas ours does not.

Philip: And I can see that if men are persuaded by Paul and Barnabas to believe that their salvation depends on no such works as we Jews are required to perform, then they will trust in Jesus alone to save them. The only question then is, does the foundation of Paul's gospel stand? Is Jesus alone the Savior of mankind? If he is, then Paul's gospel came from God, and it will outlast ours.

Eli: I will hear no more of this!

Paul: To the endangerment of your soul will you not hear it.

Simon Peter: Brother Eli, it is not wise to speak evil of things that you do not understand.

John: Brother Eli, I beg you . . .

Eli: God commanded us under penalty of death to expose anyone who tries to turn men from the law, even if it be the dearest person to us on earth![388] I understand *that!*

As God lives, if He gives me strength, I will go out from this place and expose this heresy to Israel and to the Gentiles! Yours is not the love of God for them; nor do you honor Jesus by your foul doctrine! You two devised this doctrine to draw away disciples after yourselves, and you have done it! I will not dishonor God by sitting here and hearing any more of it! I am with Hillel and Lamech! [*Eli leaves.*]

Nadab: So am I! [*Nadab leaves.*]

Counsel members: *Comments.*

Hushai: God forbid that we should allow such a "gospel" as yours, Paul, to go unchallenged among the Gentiles. We will teach them the wondrous things of the law!

Paul: You will be doing a wondrous evil if you go again to the Gentiles with the gospel that God gave only for the Jews! And the dead works you cling to will become your prison and your curse!

---

[388] Dt. 13:1–11.

Hushai: [*suddenly calm and quieter*] Doing evil by teaching the law of God to those who do not know it? I think not.

Paul: Teach them about the law all you want; I do that myself. But do not require them to keep it, Hushai, lest you make yourself the enemy of God.

Hushai: [*again, calmly*] Your threats bore me, Paul. I will take my leave now, brothers. I can stand no more of this. [*Hushai leaves.*]

Counsel members: *Comments.*

PART 4
THE COUNCIL CONCLUDES

———❦———

Hananiah and Others Are Persuaded To Stay

Hananiah: Men and brothers, I sincerely regret this division. I had hoped for better when the day began. But let me remind you of what I said in the beginning. We who are devoted to God's law did not bring this trouble and strife upon God's saints. Ours is the faith with which we all began; in it, we followed our sinless Lord Jesus to great benefit for our souls, for in doing that, we were blessed with the Spirit.

I understand what Paul and Barnabas are saying. Perhaps that is the test, that I understand it. If I did not understand it, I would probably be inclined to stay and hear more, in hope of understanding it. But as it is, brothers, I cannot. It certainly gives me pause to see that most of you, my respected brothers and elders, embrace this new doctrine. Nevertheless, I must cast my lot with those of like judgment with me, even if their harshness is not of my liking. And so, I bid you an affectionate farewell.

Jacobus: Hananiah, I beg you to re-consider.

Hananiah: Jacobus, I have done nothing but consider this matter for many days now.

Philip: We walked with Jesus together, Hananiah.

Hananiah: So did brother Uzziel, Hillel, and Hushai. They walked with us, too. So, tell me, Philip, who divided us? Did Uzziel or Hillel bring a new doctrine into the Assembly? Or Hushai?

Benjamin: Or me? Am I the guilty one?

Hananiah: Benjamin, thank you, but you do not have to leave with me. Do as your heart tells you, my friend.

Benjamin: But I have always been with you.

Silas: Brothers, the only thing that unity requires is that we acknowledge one another's calling and that each man be content in his own place.

Benjamin: Silas, sir, I am with Hananiah, and for the same reasons he has said. I feel compelled to leave with him. And I believe that you would do as we are doing if you felt as we do.

Daniel: Show Benjamin the way, Hananiah; it is your place. Fellowship is worth the price of patience. You knew at the start that we elders and apostles believed the testimony of Barnabas and Paul concerning their calling.

Hananiah: Yes, that was evident from the start.

Daniel: Nevertheless, we elders have allowed you complete liberty to question them, and we have interfered very little with your examination of them, though at times, we felt compelled to speak.

Council members: *Comments.*

Daniel: As an elder and brother in the Lord – if you see me as such – I entreat you to stay and hear Barnabas and Paul once more. I believe that Jesus will do something good for those who remain. But if after that, you still desire to go, you may go, though our hearts will be grieved for it.

Council members: *That is right. Yes, we would. Etc.*

Nahum: It would be good, Hananiah. It is right that you stay.

Hananiah: Other than in this matter, I have never doubted the wisdom of you elders as I do now. Nevertheless, I have learned by experience that I do well when I lay my thoughts aside and take yours in. I have been healed by doing that. So, I am content to do as you ask. I will stay and give ear to whatever it is you think I need to hear.

Micah: I am glad you have chosen to stay, Hananiah. We are not finished here, and I believe that we will profit by staying.

Nathan: It is good for you to do this, brothers.

Jacobus: Very well, then. Where should we begin?

Silas: I have been watching Benjamin and Maschil, Jacobus, and I think they have deferred often to their elders when they had something to say. Why not let them speak, if they want to?

Council members: *Yes. I agree. Etc.*

Benjamin: You are perceptive, sir. I have had things to say, and questions.

Maschil: I'm so confused that I have forgotten what my questions were. But I think the thing that has made this so difficult for me is that I have always equated faith in God's law with faith in God, but what Paul and the rest of you are saying is driving a sharp wedge between those two things. And it is a painful divide.

Jacobus: I understand completely, Maschil. But as Daniel wisely said, "Fellowship is worth the price of patience," and we will stay as long as it takes to resolve your questions so that we may attain to fellowship.

Council members: *Yes. I agree. Etc.*

Maschil: I just don't see why this new covenant would do away with the law, or turn it into a spiritual law, or however I should say it. Why do you say that the two covenants are mutually exclusive?

Paul: Excellent question, Maschil, and this is the answer. As I told Benjamin earlier, the covenant God made with Israel at Mount Sinai was altogether, as I say it, "in the flesh". Under the law, the flesh got everything. The feasts of God fed the flesh; the holy garments covered and adorned the flesh; the Sabbaths gave rest to the flesh; even the wars of that covenant were wars against men in the flesh. But in this covenant, our spirits get everything. Our spirits feast on invisible manna from heaven; our sacrifice is our spiritual worship, rising from pure lips and a sanctified heart; our garments are the garments of praise and righteousness; our Sabbath is rest from the dominion of sin; and our warfare is only against the invisible powers of this age, not against flesh and blood. The Lord is the Spirit, and where the Spirit of the Lord is, there is liberty from dependence on the arm of flesh, liberty from the law of carnal commandments, liberty from sin, and liberty from death itself.

John: That is beautiful, Paul. This will also help you, Maschil, and you, Benjamin. The night Jesus was arrested, he told us he had overcome the world.[389] I did not understand him then because I knew he rarely crossed the border of our country. But the Spirit has since taught me that he had, indeed, overcome the world because all that is in the world is covetousness, lust, and pride, and when he conquered those things in himself, he had conquered the whole world.

Barnabas: And consider this. Jesus did not suffer and die for something we already possessed or could already do. If we already had it or could do it, he could have stayed in heaven and spared himself much suffering. No, Jesus suffered and died to bring in a new way that was *impossible* for man before he came, and that new and living way is what God always had in mind, from the foundation of the world. Men without the life of God can perform the law's rites; indeed, they have been doing it for over a thousand years. But in this covenant, what God requires, requires God.

Andrew: We asked Jesus one time who could be saved, and he said, "With men, it is impossible."[390] We didn't know what he meant.

Philip: It frightened me.

Cleopas: It frightened all of us.

Andrew: But now, we understand. If any man does not have the Spirit, he can only worship "in the flesh", as Paul says it. Such a man cannot worship God acceptably, even if he prays and praises Him all day long. That is what Jesus was telling the Samaritan woman. Worship from

---

[389] Jn. 16:33.
[390] Mt. 19:26; Mk. 10:27.

an unsanctified spirit is unsanctified worship, and God no longer accepts it. That is why Jesus said we must be born again, in a new way.

Benjamin: That makes sense to me.

Maschil: Yes, but if what God requires, requires God, as Barnabas said, doesn't the law also require God? We could not have conceived of such a just and holy law. I apologize if I sound argumentative again, but I have that question.

Daniel: A good question is as much from God as a good answer, Maschil, and just as refreshing.

Benjamin: Daniel, sir, could you help us understand this?

Daniel: I will try.

Benjamin: I want to understand it, if it really is the truth.

Daniel: I know you do. Then, let me ask you, son, what is it about the truth that makes it the truth? What is it that is true about the truth, and why does it even matter? Have either of you young men ever considered that?

Benjamin: No, sir.

Maschil: I never had such a thought.

Daniel: The roots of faith are deep, and wisdom digs for them to discover its source of strength. The roots of our faith reach into the very heart of God, and you are being invited by the Spirit into that sacred place to search them out. Wisdom asks why God loves the truth so much that He will damn the soul who denies or defies it. Do you young men know why the truth matters that much to God? [*pauses*]

Maschil: No.

Benjamin: No, sir.

Council members: *Quiet.*

Daniel: Then I will tell you why. The truth matters that much because the truth is not a thing. The truth is the Son of God, and God dearly loves His Son. Messiah Jesus is what makes the truth the truth; he defines it in himself, and there is no truth apart from him. That is why whoever refuses Jesus is a fool.

Maschil: Forgive me, I beg you, but I must point out again that no prophet ever said what you are saying.

Daniel: No prophet *could* say what I am saying, son; this comes from the life of God, and no prophet had it. Long ago, the Son of God moved the prophet to say, "All who hate me love death,"[391] and I assure you, they will have it. Jesus told us plainly when he was among us that he himself

---

[391] Prov. 8:36.

was the truth of God,[392] but we did not understand him. However, after the Spirit of God came, we learned that it is the Son that is the truth; he himself is the living truth of God.

Before the Son was revealed, God gave men hints about His Son until the appointed time, and those holy hints were the only truth we had. Nevertheless, God loved His Son so much that He demanded that we reverence those hints. But He did not intend for us to reverence the hints forever, for He knew the time would come when His Son would shine upon us and the true, eternal way of life would be revealed. The law and the prophets were hints about the Son, though neither Moses nor the prophets knew that is what they were. Creation itself was a hint about the Son because God created all things through him, but no one in creation understood this because no one in creation knew the Son even existed before God sent him here and revealed him.

No lies were hints about the Son, and every lie was a lie against him; therefore, God gave us a law that forbade lying. Nothing proud was a hint, no murder, no wicked thought or desire, no false witness, and no trouble maker.[393] Whatever was not a God-given hint about His Son was not the truth, and God despised it, and He condemned those in Israel who lived contrary to the hints He had given for our sakes.

Benjamin: But why, if the hints were not God's Son, did God destroy those who walked contrary to *them?*

Daniel: Excellent, son. A question is wisdom's spade.

With the law, God painted a picture of His Son *for our sakes,* to prepare us to recognize him when he came, and God was indignant, for our sakes, when any man dared to tamper with the picture He had painted. He struck Nadab and Abihu dead for our sakes when they offered strange fire at His tabernacle, and He cursed King Uzziah with leprosy for our sakes when he defied God's priesthood and entered into the temple to offer incense himself. Indeed, He destroyed this nation and carried the people into captivity for our sakes when they refused to walk according to His hints and rejected His prophets and their calls to heed the hints. Refusing the hints that God gave of His beloved, but as yet hidden Son is what made transgression of the law sin; whatever was contrary to the hints God gave was rebellion against His Son because those hints were about the Son.

---

[392] Jn. 14:6.
[393] Cf. Prov. 6:16–19.

David told us that God hates the wicked who walk contrary to Moses' law,[394] but we say now that God considers them wicked who walk contrary to His Son and that He hates them! In this covenant, God hates *whatever is not His Son* instead of hating whatever is not a hint about him, for the Son has come and has given us the Spirit of God,[395] and where the Spirit of the Lord is, there is liberty from hints, for the truth has come! Only what is in His Son is acceptable to God, and the hints God gave Israel were holy only because they were hints about His Son.

The gospel is not something *about* the Son, as the hints were. The gospel is in power, not talk, for the gospel is the Son himself, and whatever is not in the Son is not the gospel. Every wise man counts all things as dung, even what was once holy, for the treasure and great honor of knowing the Son of God! The Son means everything to God and everything to us! *Jesus* is our "law and prophets"; Jesus is our ark of testimony; he is our circumcision and baptism, and our one great hope. He is our Passover, and we are his firstfruits to God. The Son is our "song in the night,"[396] and it is sin to sing any other song in God's Assembly. The hints God once gave us were other songs, for they were songs *about* him, but now, he himself sings his song through the Spirit among the brothers! As he begged the Father through David before he was revealed: "Let me declare your name to my brothers! In the midst of the congregation, let me praise you!" And now, God has allowed him to sing, and any other song but his in the Assembly of God is a lie and does not belong! Every singer is a liar if the Spirit is not confessing the Son through him when he sings in the Assembly. Every dancer is a liar if the Spirit is not confessing the Son through him when he dances in the Assembly. Every prophet is a liar if the Spirit is not confessing the Son through him when he prophesies. And every preacher is a liar if the Spirit is not confessing the Son through him when he preaches. As the scripture said, "I have believed; therefore, I have spoken!"[397] We believe in him; therefore, we speak by him! The Son was once the Father's best-kept secret, and now, the Son is His best revelation!

Council members: *Comments.*

Daniel: Under the law, whatever was not *about* the Son was sin; now, however, whatever is not the Son himself is sin. There is no sin or darkness in the Son, but outside the Son is nothing but sin and darkness, and

---

[394] Cf. Ps. 5:5; 11:5.
[395] Jn. 14:23.
[396] Job 35:10; Ps. 77:6.
[397] Ps. 116:10.

God has sworn to destroy it all and create for us a new heaven and a new earth.

Council members: *Comments*.

Daniel: Brothers, Jesus has ascended into heaven and is sitting at the Father's right hand, and there is now nothing holy on this earth except the holy Spirit that God sent in His Son's stead. Whatever is not in the Spirit is not of God, including life according to the ancient hints that God gave. To live that way now is rebellion against the Son; it is to deny his work. The revelation of the Son has made even those ancient, glorious hints about him vain, for *they* are not *him*. How much better it is, brothers, to have the Son dwelling in our hearts than for us to still be dwelling in the shadows of his light, waiting for him to come – shadows that we never even understood were shadows until he came and told us.

Council members: *Comments*.

Daniel: Abraham worshipped God as was right in his own eyes, for there was no law to guide him; God had not yet given men that hint. The law was added later to deal with sin, to warn men of the Judgment to come and to foreshadow the hidden, righteous Judge into whose hands God had given all judgment.[398] Now, by the Spirit, we again are free to worship as we will, with this one great difference: the Son has given us an anointing to know the will of God, so that what is good in God's eyes may also be good in ours.

Benjamin: That is a frightening liberty, sir, to be free to do as we will.

Daniel: Yes, but good hearts, like Abraham, lived according to the hints God gave, before He gave them. Joseph, too, had no law from God that said, "Do not commit adultery." Joseph could have committed adultery with Potiphar's wicked wife and then tried to deny his guilt by saying, "Where is the law wherein God commanded us not to commit adultery?" But even when the law came, what did we find? We found that sinners kept sinning under the law, but hid secret sins behind *obedience* to the forms of the law.[399] They hid their sin in the holy shadow of God's Son! So, before the Son was revealed, sin always found a hiding place because man himself was not free from sin, no matter how holy God's hints were.

But now, Benjamin, sin has no more hiding place, for the Son has made whatever is of God – His power, and goodness, and truth – freely available in the Spirit. Therefore, sin has no more excuse, and no more hiding place. There is nothing more frightening to ungodly souls than lib-

---

[398] Jn. 5:22.
[399] Isa. 1:10–15.

erty without excuse, and by giving us perfect liberty, Jesus has done away with all excuse for sin. That is why Jesus was hated in this world, and those who are like him will be likewise hated. As Jesus said, "If men have called the master of the house Beelzebul, how much more those of his household?"[400] True righteousness is a matter of the heart, and evil hearts hate true ones.

Do you young men understand me?

Benjamin: I think so, yes.

Maschil: Yes sir, we do.

Barnabas: Amen, Daniel. So, the law was holy, Maschil, but it was still a carnal thing, and it will pass away with all else that is carnal.

Maschil: Yes, I remember hearing Paul say that, earlier. I suppose that we need truths to be repeated when they are so new to us.

Barnabas: We all understand that.

John: One thing in particular that Jesus said reveals the difference between the covenants as well as anything I know. In the old covenant, as you know, God commanded Israel to be holy *"because* I am holy"*,*[401] but Jesus did not say that. He commanded us instead to be holy *as* God is holy.[402] Nothing in the law could make us holy *as* God is holy because it was a dead thing, all of it. But the Spirit of God makes us holy *as* God is holy, for, as we said earlier, it makes us partakers of God's holy nature.

Maschil: That is an astonishing thought.

John: Yes it is. But as He is, so are we now, in this world.

Maschil: [*quietly*] Praise God.

Benjamin: But why did God wait so long after creation to send His Son if what He wanted the whole time was only what is spiritual? Thousands of years is a long time.

Paul: God's life, and His Son who was filled with it, is so foreign to fallen man that God had to prepare men for His Son's coming. Can you see that? We were so sinful and rebellious that it took God thousands of years to make us ready. And even at that, we killed him when he came, thinking he was evil.

Benjamin: Yes.

Paul: It was only because of the influence of the law and the prophets on Israel, Benjamin, that Jesus was able to survive on earth as long as he did, once he started preaching. Any other nation on earth would have killed him much sooner. As bad as we Jews may have been, this nation

---

[400] Mt. 10:25.

[401] Lev. 11:44; 19:2.

[402] Mt. 5:48.

was the safest place on earth for God to send His sinless Son because our spirits had been tempered by His law.

Micah: Hananiah, I think our students ask better questions than we do.

Hananiah: Agreed.

Nahum: Brothers, do you understand what these men have told you?

Micah: I think we have always understood, to some degree, but we could not bring ourselves to believe what we saw. Can you understand how that could be?

Barnabas: I certainly do. But do you understand that our gospel for the Gentiles does not condemn your gospel for the Jews, as long as it is preached to the Jews?

Micah: Yes, you and Paul have made that very clear.

Hananiah: Yes, very clear.

John: Brothers, I can't help but think about Uzziel, how he and the others left. It brought back to me the day Jesus told some Pharisees, some of whom you know, Micah, that if they were children of Abraham, they would behave the way Abraham behaved . . .[403]

Philip: . . . and that if God was their Father, they would love Jesus. Jesus told them that.[404]

John: That's right.

Micah: I remember that day, John, and my friends and I discussed it later.

John: You were there? Well, what did your friends say?

Micah: Did you know that Uzziel was there also?

John: No, I didn't.

Micah: Yes. Well, we had a long discussion, and he and I decided that, yes, Abraham would have loved Jesus, and those who are like Abraham would love him, too. The others criticized us for believing that. But we just did.

Bartholomew: The grace of God was with you.

Micah: May God help my friends, too, Uzziel and the rest. We have had wonderful times together in the Lord.

Council members: *Yes, we have. God, help them! Etc.*

Benjamin: Brothers, may I ask another question?

Council members: *Please do. Of course. Etc.*

---

[403] Jn. 8:39.

[404] Jn. 8:42.

Benjamin: Just so I can be sure, brother Paul. You say that the uncircumcised who believe are children of Abraham, who was circumcised, while the circumcised who do not believe are not Abraham's children?

Paul: Yes, because they are uncircumcised in heart. Benjamin, a man is no longer a Jew in God's sight because of anything outward; nor is the circumcision of God outward in the flesh. But one becomes a Jew in God's eyes by receiving Jesus' circumcision of the heart, by the Spirit. Men will not praise you for receiving that truth, but God will.

Maschil: But when Jeremiah was pleading with Israel to repent, he said to them, "Circumcise *yourselves* to the LORD and remove the foreskin of your heart."405 Why would God have called on Israel to do something which, according to you, they could not do? Scriptures such as that, brother Paul, throw doubt on your gospel.

Paul: I understand, Maschil. But God was not calling on Israel to do something they could not do.

Maschil: But you teach that the only circumcision that counts with God is the circumcision that Jesus performs on our hearts by the Spirit, and they could not do that. Is that not right?

Paul: That is the case now, Maschil, but under the law, until Messiah came, the prophets' call to circumcise the heart meant to change one's attitude from one of rebelliousness against God's will to one of submission. You mentioned Jeremiah calling on Israel to circumcise their hearts. In that same prophecy, you may remember, Jeremiah also called upon Israel to wash their own hearts from evil.406 But again, that was just a figurative way in those days of calling upon Israel to repent. But now, in this covenant, Jesus purges our inner man from a carnal nature so that we might serve God together in a new and living way, and we cannot do that for ourselves, no matter what rite we perform or how many commandments we obey. Jesus alone has the power to circumcise a man's soul from its natural inclination to sin, and he does it by the Spirit that he purchased for us with his blood.

Simon Peter: When we call on Israel to repent, Maschil, we are saying the same thing Jeremiah said, that is, that they must circumcise their hearts to the LORD and wash their hearts from evil, according to the law. The difference is that now, when they sanctify themselves according to the law, the Spirit comes into them and sanctifies their souls, which the law cannot do.

---

405 Jer. 4:4.
406 Jer. 4:14a.

Benjamin: Can the Gentiles circumcise their heart to the LORD or wash their hearts from evil, brother Paul? What do you tell them, since they do not have the law?

Paul: That is a perceptive question, Benjamin. The Gentiles can repent, of course, from the sins they know, even without knowing the law. Repentance being a matter of the heart, if God convicts their heart, and they believe in Jesus and turn from the sins they know, then God will mercifully cleanse their hearts by His Spirit, just as He has cleansed us in Israel who believe.

Benjamin: I see.

Paul: But what the Gentiles cannot do, Benjamin, is what God commands in Israel, that is, they cannot sanctify themselves as we Jews can. In order for sinners in Israel to receive forgiveness for their sin, they must sanctify themselves, that is, make themselves ritually clean, so that the priest will accept from them the sacrifices God has ordained for forgiveness. If they do not sanctify themselves so that their sacrifices are acceptable, they will not be forgiven.

Maschil: I understand. The Gentiles have no way to sanctify themselves or make themselves ritually clean in God's sight because their rituals were not given by God, and sacrifices to their gods, as Moses said, are sacrifices to demons, not to God.[407]

Paul: Yes, Moses and David both said that.[408] That is correct. So, when Gentiles try to repent by sanctifying themselves according to their traditional rites, they only make things worse. So, God is satisfied with heartfelt repentance from them, and He sanctifies them by His Spirit instead of demanding that they sanctify themselves first, according to Moses' law.

Simon Peter: And by that same mercy, God forgave us, though we had obeyed and sanctified ourselves.

Paul: Amen, Peter. Even though God, for the time being, still requires that of the Jews, it has always been to Him a matter of the heart, not of proper ceremonial form. Jesus came to reveal that truth about the Father.

Micah: No man can argue with these things, brothers. And in truth, I cannot now see why any man would want to. This light explains why, as I have heard you say, this is a better covenant.

Council members: *Comments.*

---

[407] Cf. Dt. 32:17.
[408] Cf. Ps. 106:37.

The Law after Jesus Returns

Hananiah: I would ask one more question. It is one to which I have not yet heard a satisfactory explanation. God said of Messiah, "He will not fail, nor be discouraged, until he has established justice on the earth, and the isles will wait for his law."[409] Now, isn't the law that the Gentiles will wait for the same law that Messiah kept while he was here?

Benjamin: Yes, and to say that such will be the case only after Jesus returns does not satisfy me, either, for some reason. Why teach the Gentiles to serve God apart from the law now if Jesus will command them to serve God under the law when he returns?

Barnabas: As we have said . . .

Nathan: Perhaps, brothers, since we agree that Jesus will send forth the law from Jerusalem when he returns, it would be good for believing Gentiles to learn to keep the law now, *before* the Lord returns. That way, when Jesus arrives, believing Gentiles will already have learned to serve God the way Jesus will command them to.

Cleopas: That is not the answer, Nathan.

Nathan: It was just a thought. Just a thought.

John: We desire unity, Nathan; indeed, we must have it. But the fellowship we need is not a fellowship we manufacture for convenience because we cannot otherwise agree. We need fellowship with one another in the healing light of God instead of an accommodation with ignorance, a compromise with darkness. I commend your desire to find a path for peace among the brothers, but if we wait on the Lord, he will show us where the true path lies. To agree to disagree is not fellowship; it is division by another name.

Nathan: I understand, John; you are right, of course. Forgive me for interrupting you, Barnabas. Continue, please.

Barnabas: I think I was about to say that the law of this covenant is an internal standard set by God in the hearts of His children. It is the nature of God, and Jesus will govern us forever by it who have partaken of that nature through the Spirit. We are submitting to that law when we walk in the Spirit, and we are being governed by it every time that gentle voice speaks in our hearts, saying, "This is the way; walk in it." That is how the Son of God has always lived with the Father, and there has never been a shadow of division between them. And if we walk in the Spirit together, there will never be a division between us, either.

---

[409] Isa. 42:4.

Hananiah: Yes, I can see that, but my question concerned the time after Jesus returns.

Barnabas: Oh yes, you were asking about the Gentiles after Jesus returns. You are right, the nations will not have the Spirit and will not know God's will by nature; therefore, Jesus will have to issue them commands that they can understand and obey without having the Spirit.

Micah: So, you are saying that Jesus will continue to communicate God's will to us through the Spirit after he comes, but he will communicate God's will to the nations by giving them commandments that they can comprehend without having the Spirit?

Barnabas: Yes, just as the prophets said. The nations will come to Jerusalem to honor Messiah, and he will give them his law, and they will be judged by the law he gives them.

Hananiah: And the laws that Jesus gives the nations at that time will be the laws as Moses wrote them?

Barnabas: I would assume so, for what law could be more perfect than that one?

Paul: Still, we will have to wait and see. He will do as God wills, whatever that may be.

Barnabas: Yes, we cannot speak with perfect certainty about things as yet unknown, but it does appear that way to me.

========

Conclusion

Narrator: This has only been a suggested version of the Acts 15 Council in Jerusalem, but I am confident that it reflects at least some of the thoughts and passions involved. The matter of Gentiles and the law was of supreme importance to the body of Christ, and yet, it was one for which there could be no resolution based solely on the scriptures, since men on both sides could make effective arguments from them. Which side the listeners took depended entirely on their hearts. Where there was pride in being a Jew, or fear of not being one, Paul's gospel would find no place.

At the very end of the meeting, after all arguments had been made, Peter arose, and when all voices were still, he spoke. Peter quoted no prophet and brought up no point of law. Nor did he refer to anything Jesus said or did while he was on earth. Peter only testified again of what God did through him at Cornelius' house, and his simple, sincere testimony left the Council with nothing else to say:

Simon Peter: Men and brothers, *you* know that a good while ago, God made choice among us, that by my mouth the Gentiles were to hear the word of the gospel, and believe. And God, who knows the heart, bore them witness, giving them the holy Spirit just as He had given it to us in the beginning, and He made no distinction between us and them, purifying their hearts by faith without the law. Now then, why would you tempt God by placing a yoke on the neck of the Lord's uncircumcised disciples which neither our fathers nor we have been able to bear? No! We believe we will be saved the same way they will be – through the grace of the Lord Jesus.[410]

Micah: I have nothing to add, brothers. It is the work of God.

Hananiah: Yes, and I thank you all. Barnabas, I hope to have more time with you and Paul before you return to Antioch.

Paul: As God wills, yes.

Barnabas: That would be a pleasure for us. Benjamin and Maschil, have your questions been answered?

Benjamin: I think so, yes. My spirit is not troubled as before.

Maschil: Yes, sir. I believe they have been, though I feel there is much yet to be learned.

Silas: That is true for us all, Maschil. And if God grants us the humility to take in the wisdom He gives, we will behold together the glory of His Son.

Daniel: Fellowship in the light of Jesus is the sweetest shadow cast by God's love. It is a great blessing, and greatly to be desired.

Counsel members: *Comments.*

Nahum: So now, men and brothers, we must teach these things to the Assemblies in Judah. And we must teach them soon, for I fear that if we do not, much trouble lies ahead for the saints of God.

Paul: We should pray, brothers, for the Assemblies of God everywhere.

Micah: . . . and for our friends. They have much zeal, but without this understanding, they will do much harm and subvert the faith of many.

Council members: *Amen! Praise God! Etc. [Someone begins another hymn. Everyone joins in.]*[411]

---

[410] Acts 15:7–11.

[411] "Our Messiah Came at Last" by Gary B. Savelli.

1

Messiah was the one we waited for.
And the prophets spoke, "The testimony and the law."
God's promises came to pass, and God's word to us stood fast.
Unto Israel, our Messiah came at last!

Chorus

He is Jesus! Our Messiah came at last!
He is Jesus! Our Messiah came at last!
Now we worship Him, the holy Lamb who died for sin.
He is Jesus! Our Messiah came at last!
His name is Jesus! Our Messiah came at last!

2

Messiah was the anointed of the Lord.
Our deliverer, out of Judah, he sprang forth.
He took our sins and shame; by His stripes, our healing came.
Unto Israel, our Messiah came at last! [Chorus]

3

Messiah was our high priest, God's own Son.
When the Spirit came, it revealed God's hidden One.
In Him all wisdom dwells, and all knowledge is beheld.
Unto Israel, our Messiah came at last! [Chorus]

4

Messiah was Israel's true Passover Lamb.
And His blood was shed, offered up for fallen man.
And on us God's face will shine, for Messiah is our light.
He is Jesus! Our Messiah came at last!

Chorus

He is Jesus! Our Messiah came at last!
He is Jesus! Our Messiah came at last!
How we worship Him, the holy Lamb who died for sin.
He is Jesus! Our Messiah came at last!
He is Jesus! Our Messiah came at last!
His name is Jesus! Our Messiah came at last!

Council members: *Amen! Praise God! Etc.*

———

Narrator: At the conclusion of the Jerusalem Council, those present listened in silence a Paul and Barnabas told of the miracles and wonders God had worked among the Gentiles by their hand.[412] Paul's wisdom and vision of the unity which God purposed in Christ, the unity which God creates through the Spirit, is given no better expression than that which is found in his letter to the believing Gentiles in Ephesus.[413] Let us imagine, then, that Paul shared the wisdom contained in those verses with the Jerusalem Council that day:

Paul: Men and brothers, hear my final word before we ask leave of you to return to Antioch to bring them the report of this meeting, for they are most anxious to hear it.

David prophesied that Messiah would prepare a feast and send forth his servants to proclaim, "Whoever is unwise, let him turn in here. Come and eat of my bread, and drink of the wine I have mixed. Forsake the foolish, and live! And walk in the way of understanding!"[414] To this feast, God invites us all today, as He now invites all men everywhere.

By the Spirit, David also said the household of God would be built upon seven pillars.[415] He said the first of the seven pillars of the house of God is the one GOD who is above all. The second pillar is the one LORD of heaven and earth, Messiah Jesus. The third pillar is the one SPIRIT by which we were all baptized, Jew and Gentile alike, into the family of God. That one BAPTISM is the fourth pillar, and that family is the fifth pillar, the one BODY of believers. Everyone in that body shares the one HOPE of eternal life, which is the sixth pillar. And the right understanding of these six pillars is the seventh: the one FAITH that will endure forever, the only gospel that is not divided against itself – my gospel for the Gentiles! This is the feast God has prepared for us, and upon this foundation alone is the household of faith rightly built. This is the new and living way created by God through Jesus, and only in this way will God's children ever be made one in the unifying bond of peace.

In the gospel for the Jews, however, the gospel which still applies to every one of us here today, except brother Titus, there are two of all these things. The gospel for the Jews recognizes two bodies as being of God: the Israel descended from Abraham's flesh, and the Israel of God who are born of the Spirit out of every nation. Every one of us in this Council to-day belongs to both these bodies, but only one of them will endure forev-

---

[412] Acts 15:12.

[413] Eph. 4:4–6.

[414] Prov. 9:2–6.

[415] Prov. 9:1.

er.   The gospel for the Circumcision also recognizes two baptisms: the baptism of the flesh that God sent John to preach to Israel, and the baptism of the Spirit that Jesus ministers from heaven to men everywhere who believe.   Only one baptism will endure; the other will soon pass away.   Also in the gospel of the Jews are two Lords: one on earth, that is, the high priest of Israel, and one in heaven, our High Priest who sits at the Father's right hand.   We acknowledge the authority of both, and submit to both for the time being, but only one Lord will continue forever; the other priesthood will pass away.   In your gospel for the Jews, there are also two hopes: the first is the hope which you who walked with Jesus thought he had come to give us, namely, an earthly kingdom.   The second hope is the hope of eternal life, for which he actually came.   In your gospel, two spirits lead men, for the spirit of man can worship in the rites of the law, but in God's kingdom, acceptable worship is worship in His Spirit alone.   In the Jews' gospel are also two faiths: faith in both the law and the power of Jesus to save.   And finally, brothers – hear me well! – for those who continue in Peter's gospel for the Jews after God finishes with it, there will soon be two Gods!   For just as those who continued to worship in high places after God chose Jerusalem were actually worshipping demons and not God, so when God finishes with the law, those who continue to worship in it will also be worshipping demons and not God.

That is what Messiah taught me.   Beware that you listen to his voice and that you do not continue in the thing God leaves behind, when that day comes!   For if you do, you will become slanderers of the truth, not ministers of it, by your works denying the very sufficiency of Jesus to save.

Now, my dear brothers, we bid you farewell, and we commend you to God until He grants that we return to be among you again.

Jacobus: We look forward to that time, brother Paul.   And Barnabas, we look forward to your return to this, your adopted home.   We bid godspeed to you and the elders from Antioch, and to you, brother Titus.   And we send our love to the brothers in Antioch.   But first, stay and let us conclude our business.

Men and brothers, Simon Peter has described how God first intervened to take from the Gentiles a people for His name.   And to this, the words of the prophets agree, for God promised that He would raise up His Son Jesus from the dead and restore him to his former glory[416] "so that the rest of mankind may seek the LORD, even all the Gentiles upon whom my

---

[416] Amos 9:11.

name is called, says the LORD who is doing all these things."[417]   Therefore, my judgment is that we not trouble those from the Gentiles who turn to God, but that we write to them to keep away from the pollutions of idols, and from immorality, and from what is strangled, and from blood, for the sake of the conscience of the Jews who live about them.   For from early times, Moses has had in every city those who preach him, being read in the synagogues every Sabbath.[418]

Narrator: Jacobus' judgment pleased the apostles and elders, and the whole Council decided to send Paul and Barnabas, along with Silas and another brother named Judas,[419] back to Antioch with a letter confirming the Council's judgment.   Their letter to Antioch contained this message:

Scribe: "The apostles and elders, and the brothers, to the Antiochan, Syrian, and Cilician brothers who are of the Gentiles. Greetings. Inasmuch as we have heard that certain men among us, to whom we gave no charge, went out from here and troubled you with words, unsettling your souls, saying you must be circumcised and keep the law, it seemed good to us, being of one mind, to send chosen men to you with our beloved Barnabas and Paul, men who have risked their lives for the name of Messiah Jesus. So, we have sent Judas and Silas, and they will tell you the same things by word of mouth. For it seemed good to the holy Spirit, and to us, to put upon you no greater burden, except for these necessary things: abstain from meats offered to idols, and from blood and what is strangled, and from immorality. Keeping yourselves from these things, you will do well. Farewell."[420]

Narrator: That letter put the controversy to rest – *for that day.*

---

[417] The origin of this quote is unknown. Perhaps it is a combination of several verses from the prophets.

[418] Acts 15:13–21.

[419] Acts 15:27.

[420] Acts 15:23–29.

PART 5
THE APOSTASY OF THE BODY OF CHRIST

—❦—

The letter from James to the Assembly in Antioch put the controversy to rest for that time and place, but as I will now show from the New Testament books, the men who opposed Paul's gospel did not give up their efforts to promote obedience to the law, and they eventually won the hearts of God's people everywhere.

The Old Is Better

The law and Peter's gospel were inextricably entwined, and within a few generations after Pentecost, they faded out together – so far as heaven was concerned. But as for the men who opposed Paul, they insisted that the law and Peter's gospel were still in force, and forever would be. Even before Paul died, such men were going to the Gentile congregations that Paul had established, in order to, as they saw it, rescue them from Paul's self-made doctrine.

Paul taught the Gentiles that in this covenant there is for them only one baptism, the baptism of the Spirit administered by Christ,[421] but the teachers of Peter's gospel would point them to the example of Jesus' disciples, all of whom had followed the Lord's example of submitting to John's baptism in water. Paul taught the Gentiles that in Christ, there are no holy days,[422] but the Jewish teachers would ask his Gentile converts why, if that was true, did Jesus observe the holy days of the law, and why were his disciples still observing them? Paul taught the Gentiles that if they received the Spirit, they were free from the law,[423] but the teachers of Peter's gospel could quote Jesus' command to his disciples to do whatever the leaders of the Jews told them to do.[424] Paul taught that circumcision is spiritual[425] and that physical circumcision no longer counts for anything with God,[426] but the teachers of Peter's gospel could point out that no such

---

[421] Eph. 4:5; 1Cor. 12:13.
[422] Col. 2:16–17.
[423] Gal. 5:18.
[424] Mt. 23:2–3.
[425] Rom. 2:28–29; Phip. 3:3.
[426] Gal. 6:15.

doctrine had ever been taught by anyone before Paul – and in saying that, they were correct.

What were the Gentiles to do? Whom were they to believe? The Jewish teachers were Spirit-filled, too, and were impressive men, adept at using the Scriptures. They could, moreover, point to every soul that God had considered righteous since Moses as examples of keeping the law, including Jesus.

No New Testament scriptures existed when Paul began preaching, and so, he could only use Old Testament scriptures to explain his revelation. That is not an impediment if one's eyes have been open, as Paul's were, but it means that in order to believe Paul, one had to receive grace from God to see it. Otherwise, the truths hidden by God in the law and the prophets could not be perceived, and the arguments of the false teachers would seem right. The sole basis for Paul's authority to preach his gospel was personal experience, that is, his being anointed by Jesus with miracle-working power and a revelation of a new gospel.

Nothing about Paul's gospel was tradition or ceremony, and nothing was of human origin. Paul's gospel came from revelation, and it depended upon revelation to be understood. Without a revelation, Paul himself would not have believed his gospel, and without a revelation, no one else can believe it. Paul could not talk anyone into believing his gospel; that is not how it is understood. Knowing that his Gentile converts would never understand him unless they heard from God for themselves, Paul exhorted them to trust in God's power rather than in the erudite speech of men.[427] He told them, "I do not cease making mention of *you* in my prayers, that God might give *you* a spirit of wisdom and of revelation in His knowledge,[428]

Jesus told his disciples before he suffered that he had many things to tell them that they would not be able to bear until after the Spirit came.[429] Paul's gospel was the chief secret that Jesus was keeping from them. Had the collective Jewish conscience been able to bear it when God revealed His Son, they would have dispensed with the lifeless symbols which foreshadowed him.[430] After all, what good is the wrapper once the candy has been taken out and eaten? The wrapper's only value is in what it hides from view. After the candy is brought out and consumed, the wrapper becomes trash. So it was with the law, but the Jews' spiritually

---

427 Eph. 5:18; 1Cor. 2:5.

428 Eph. 1:15–17.

429 Jn. 16:12–13.

430 This is what Paul was teaching in 2Corinthians 3:7–11.

immature conscience could not bear that truth. And so, although the Son was worthy of exclusive and absolute devotion, God did not demand that Israel immediately cease from the wrapper of the law when He revealed His Son. Jesus said in one of his parables, "No one wants new wine immediately after drinking the old, for he says, 'The old is better'" (Lk. 5:39). This is how it was for Jewish believers when they heard the new gospel that Paul preached. To them, the old was better.

It was also difficult for believers among the Jews to accept Paul's gospel because the apostles were still preaching the gospel Jesus had preached, and because God was confirming the apostles' preaching with signs and miracles.[431] Why would God send another gospel, they might have asked, when the first one was working just fine? And there was another compelling reason that believing Jews clung to the wrapper as well as the candy, that is, they knew that their devotion to the wrapper, the law, was the very thing about them that had pleased God and had prepared them for His Son. Knowing that, it was all but impossible for them to believe that Paul could be doing the right thing by refusing to preach the law to the Gentiles.

The gospel that Jesus and the first apostles preached to the Jews required believers to cling to the wrapper as well as to eat the candy. But that gospel suggested that salvation required the law as well as faith in Jesus. Paul's unexpected gospel of throwing away the wrapper shocked all the Jews who heard it, including the believers among them. It seemed supremely sacrilegious. Only with a touch from God could they ever believe that Christ would do away with the very thing about them that had pleased God and made their nation distinct from the heathen.

Evidence of the Apostasy from Paul's Letters

Paul failed to save God's Assemblies from the wolves who came to them in sheep's clothing.[432] In the beginning, the wolves were Jewish, but at the close of the apostolic era, there were many Gentile wolves ravishing God's flock along with them. To fully comprehend this, we must rid ourselves of the mythological Jesus of Christian tradition, along with Christianity's mythological Paul, whose glorious presence supposedly overawed believers. The real Jesus had no halo or any other physical appeal (Isa. 53:2), and the real Paul neither impressed nor intimidated anyone with his presence (2Cor. 10:10). And we must also rid ourselves

---

[431] Mk. 16:20.

[432] As Paul predicted in Acts 20:29.

of Christianity's mythological Peter, before whom God's people supposedly stood in awe; it was never that way with Peter. He was not even the head of the Assembly of God in Jerusalem; James was. And when Peter's behavior displeased the elders of that congregation, they had no qualms about rebuking him (Acts 11:2–3).

Saving faith is not blind; it is based upon facts and reasonable conclusions based upon those facts. It is true, for example, that Abraham left his native land "not knowing where he was going," but his leaving was based upon the concrete fact that God told him to go. Abraham was not walking in darkness, hoping he was doing the right thing. His faith was based on a genuine experience with God, not superstition. Facts may be overlooked, ignored, or forgotten, or, if one is blinded by desire that something other than the truth be true, facts may even be denied. Nevertheless, facts never surrender to pressure for them to become non-factual. As John Adams famously said, "Facts are stubborn things, and whatever may be our wishes, our inclinations, or the dictates of our passions, they cannot alter the state of facts or evidence."[433]

So, as contrary as it may be to our "wishes, inclinations, or passions," it is a stubborn fact that Paul ended his life *persona non grata* among the majority of believers. His situation mirrored that of the prophets, who were often despised and persecuted in their own time, but later were highly praised by equally wicked generations (cp. Mt. 23:29–31). Hypocrites have always honored dead men of God; it's the living ones they hate. As an aged prisoner in Rome, the real apostle Paul lamented that some of his closest fellow-workers had abandoned him, naming Demas, Crescens, and even his dearly beloved Titus (2Tim. 4:10). But the infidelity of those brothers pales in comparison to the apostasy of the entire body of Christ within the Roman province of Asia. They all – just think of it – they all repudiated Paul and the gospel that he had taught them (2Tim. 1:15). Among those congregations were the seven Assemblies mentioned in John's Revelation (Rev. 2–3), most notably the Assembly in Ephesus. The Colossian Assembly was also in Asia, but in Revelation, Jesus sent no message there. The pastor and congregation in Colossae most likely had fallen into such apostasy by that time as to warrant neither a warning nor an exhortation such as Jesus sent to the pastors in Asia that he still recognized as his.

---

[433] Frederic Kidder, *History of the Boston Massacre, March 5, 1770; Consisting of the Narrative of the Town, the Trial of the Soldiers* [...] (New York: Joel Munsell, 1870), 258. This was part of his brilliant courtroom defense of British soldiers accused of murder in what was afterward called "The Boston Massacre".

But even when Paul was in his prime, judging by his letters, the abysmal spiritual condition of believers in Asia was mirrored by that of believers in other places. The following survey of New Testament books will show that Paul was forced to spend much time and effort trying to persuade his own Gentile converts of the legitimacy of his gospel for them.

Galatians

Paul was surprised at how quickly the Galatians had been persuaded to forsake his gospel of grace for a gospel of works, "which is not a [legitimate gospel for *you* Gentiles], but there are certain men who trouble *you*, determined to change the gospel of Christ" (1:6–7). In this letter, Paul felt the need to remind the Galatians that he was an apostle "not of men, nor by man, but by Jesus Christ and God the Father who raised him from the dead" (1:1). That introduction to his letter was not a mere form; it was part of Paul's defense against false teachers. Paul went on to remind these saints that his new gospel came by revelation: "I'd have *you* to know, brothers, regarding the gospel delivered by me, that it is not of man. I did not receive it from man, nor was I taught it, but it came by a revelation from Jesus Christ" (1:11–12). The Galatians heard those things the first time Paul preached to them, and the fact that Paul felt the need to repeat it tells us much about what these Gentiles were hearing about Paul and what they had begun to think about him.

The mythological Paul of Christianity would never have had to plead with his converts to love him or to believe him, but the real Paul was driven to swear an oath in an effort to win them back: "The things I am writing to *you* – behold, before God! – I am not lying!" (1:20). This real Paul felt the need to let the Galatians know that he had contended openly with Jewish brothers who opposed his gospel (2:4–5), that the apostles in Jerusalem acknowledged his gospel as being from God (2:1–3, 6–10), and that he had publicly rebuked Peter for making believing Gentiles feel like second-class citizens in God's kingdom (2:11–14). The real Paul had to remind the Galatians of how much they used to love him, and had to humbly ask, "Have I now become *your* enemy because I tell *you* the truth?" (4:12–16). And knowing that those who preached Peter's gospel to the Galatians had told them of his former cruelty to the saints, the real Paul was forced to bring up that painful memory and admit to that sin (1:13–14). However, he added to the story something which the Jewish teachers would have craftily left out, namely, that the Assemblies in Judea which once feared Paul now glorified God because of him (1:22–24).

Paul also warned his beloved Galatians that they were being flattered by Jewish teachers so that they would, in turn, look up to them and desire to be like them (4:17), that is, to be circumcised and submit to the law.

Paul's warnings came too late for some. They had already begun to observe the law's holy days, which means that at least some of them had already submitted to circumcision. Paul was distraught. "*You* observe days and months and seasons and years. I am afraid for *you*, that I may have labored among *you* in vain" (4:10–11). "My little children, for whom I am suffering labor pains again until Christ be formed within *you*, I desire to be with *you* now and to change my tone, for I am unsettled about *you*" (4:19–20). "*You* were running well," Paul lamented. "Who hindered *you* from obeying the truth?" (5:7).

Near the end of his letter, Paul warned the Galatians of two hidden motives of their new teachers: (1) they wanted to put on an impressive show and (2) they wanted to boast about how many converts to their gospel they had made (6:12–13). Paul knew that those teachers were using the Galatians' love for God against them by teaching them that love for God expresses itself by submission to Moses' law. But the false teachers would have argued in turn that Paul was using the Galatians' ignorance of Moses' law to promote himself.

Finally, in his closing remarks, the grieving man of God uttered a blessing on those who were faithful to his gospel, those who put no confidence in ceremonial worship and were content to live and worship in the Spirit as new creatures in Christ Jesus (6:16).

Colossians

In his letter to the saints in Colossae, Paul emphasized, as usual, the absolute sufficiency of Christ to save. And as in his other letters to Gentile believers, what Paul did *not* say comforted and encouraged his Readers as much as what he did write. For example, when Paul told them that they had forgiveness of sins because they were in Christ (1:14), it would have stood out to the Colossians that Paul did *not* say they had forgiveness of sins because they were in Christ *and kept the law*. That omission means nothing to modern readers, but it strengthened the believers in Colossae against the pressure to be circumcised. Their faith was also strengthened when Paul reminded them that all of God's wisdom and knowledge are hidden in Christ, not in Christ *and the law* (Col. 2:3).

Especially comforting to these Gentiles was Paul's frequent use of "we" and "us". With those two little words, Paul was making a powerful statement, for he was saying that God did not recognize the "us and them" attitude and doctrine of Jewish teachers. "The Father has made *us* fit", Paul wrote, "to receive an inheritance of saints," and has "delivered *us* from the domain of darkness and translated *us* into the kingdom of His beloved Son," so that in Christ, "*we* have redemption" (1:12–13). This would have meant much to the Colossians because Paul was a Jewish believer speaking to Gentile believers as if they were all one, unlike the Jewish teachers they had heard. Paul explained that God had done these things because, through the death of His Son, He had done away with the law which divided Jews from Gentiles (2:14). Paul insisted that *everyone* who receives the Spirit (with nothing added to that experience) is one of the chosen people of God (3:12). Paul also taught them that the great mystery which God kept secret from the beginning of the world was His plan for the Son to dwell in the hearts of Gentiles as well as Jews by the Spirit, *not by the Spirit and the law* (1:26–27). And finally, Paul told them that he was suffering for their sakes, that is, he was suffering for the gospel that Jesus had given him for them (2:1–2).

Paul implored these saints to continue to live in the uncircumcised state in which they received Christ (2:6). "*You* are complete in him!" Paul demanded, explaining that "*you* are circumcised with a circumcision performed without hands . . . the circumcision of Christ!" (2:10–11). "Therefore, do not allow anyone to condemn *you* in matters of eating and drinking, or in regard to a feast, or a new moon, or a Sabbath, which are a shadow of things to come, but the reality is of Christ" (2:16–17). He told these Gentiles that when they were baptized into Christ by the Spirit, they had died, been buried, and were resurrected with him (2:12; 3:3). And if that is the case, he argued, they should not even consider submitting to the law's handwritten ordinances such as, "Do not touch! Do not taste! Do not handle!" (2:20–21). Instead, having been spiritually raised up with Christ to God's right hand, they should seek spiritual things from heaven, where Christ now lives (3:1–3).

Paul felt the need to write these things to the Colossians "so that no one will be able to beguile *you* with specious argument" (2:4),which comment reveals Paul's mind, that he was trying to equip these saints to face the false teachers he knew were trying to win them over to a different gospel.

Philippians

Here, Paul condemned those who brought Peter's gospel to the Gentiles as "evil workers", and he warned the Philippian saints to "beware of circum-mutilation, for we are the circumcision, who serve God in spirit, and boast in Christ Jesus, and do not trust in the flesh" (3:2b–3). The Gentiles had been referring to circumcision as mutilation for hundreds of years,[434] but for Paul, himself a circumcised Jew, to do so must have astonished the Philippians. But by this time, Paul was exasperated by the stubborn opposition he had to face from believing as well as unbelieving Jews, and he had come to despise Jewish pride in being God's chosen people, and in their physical circumcision, sacrifices, and ancestry, etc., which they felt made them forever superior to all other people. Whereas Jesus referred to uncircumcised Gentiles as "dogs", Paul calls Jews, *even believing Jews*, dogs who rejected his gospel of the sufficiency of Christ to save men's souls (3:2a).

In the third chapter of Philippians, Paul's phrase "in the flesh" is used to describe worship according to the law. It was to the rituals of the law that Paul was referring when he said, "I have good reason to trust in the flesh. If anyone else thinks he has reason to trust in the flesh, I have more: circumcised the eighth day; of the nation of Israel; of the tribe of Benjamin; a Hebrew of the Hebrews; concerning the law, a Pharisee; concerning zeal, persecuting the Assembly of God; being blameless according to the righteousness that is in the law" (3:4–6). All of that, however, was considered by Paul to be mere garbage in comparison to the possession of the true knowledge of God, for the truth of Christ enabled him to please God by "not having my own righteousness, which is of the law, but that righteousness which is by the faith of Christ, the righteousness of God, based on faith" (3:8–11).

Ephesians

The Ephesians were not yet troubled by Jewish teachers of Peter's gospel, but that they were in danger of being taken in is evidenced by how much time Paul spent dealing with that issue in this letter. Paul's famous statement to the Ephesians, "*You* are saved by grace, through faith," continues with "this is not of *y*ourselves; it is the gift of God, not of works, lest anyone should boast" (2:8–9). The works that Paul said played no part in salvation were the ceremonial rites of Moses' law, such as circumcision, holy days, sacrifices, and so forth. That Jesus saves by the Spirit alone, without works of the law, was the heart of Paul's gospel, and the Ephesian believers understood perfectly what he meant.

---

[434] Among Greeks and Romans, circumcision was often condemned as senseless mutilation. The ancient physician Galen even praised the foreskin as one of nature's adornments for the male body (*Galen: On the Usefulness of the Parts of the Body*, ed. and trans. Margaret Tallmadge May, 2 vols. (Ithaca: Cornell University Press, 1968), 2:529).

Paul told these Gentiles that because Jesus had circumcised their hearts by the Spirit, they were no longer considered "the uncircumcised", except by the Jews (2:11). Before they received the Spirit, Paul acknowledged, they were "strangers to the covenants of promise, having no hope and without God in the world. But now, in Christ Jesus [not by the law], they had been brought near [to the true God] by the blood of Christ [not by works of the law]" (2:12–13). Jesus once said he did not come to destroy the law (Mt. 5:17), but Paul told these Gentiles that Jesus had destroyed it and that by doing so, he had done away with the difference between Jew and Gentiles in the sight of God: "He is our peace, who made of the two [i.e., Jew and Gentile] one and destroyed the dividing partition, the enmity in his flesh, the law of commandments contained in ordinances, nullifying it so that he might make of those two [Jews and Gentiles] one new man in himself, thus making peace, and that he might reconcile them both to God in one body through the cross" (2:14–16a). "We both", Paul said, "have access to the Father by one Spirit. So then, *you* are no longer strangers and foreigners, but fellow citizens with the saints, and members of the household of God" (Eph. 2:18–19).

Paul exhorted these saints to believe "that by revelation, the mystery was made known to me . . . which in other generations was not made known to the sons of men" (3:3b, 5a), and this mystery was this: "the Gentiles are to be heirs with *the Jews*, and of the same body, and partakers together of His promise in Christ, through the gospel [not through the law]" (3:6). "To me," he wrote, "the least of all saints, was this grace given, to preach among the Gentiles the incomprehensible richness of Christ" (3:8). Still, the pressure remained on these saints in Ephesus, and on others everywhere, to think that Jesus was not so rich.

1 Thessalonians

Like the Ephesian Assembly, the Thessalonian saints seemed to be doing well when Paul wrote their letters. However, also like the Ephesians, the danger of false teachers was present. For this reason, Paul stressed that, unlike false teachers who would turn these saints to another gospel, he had not flattered them when he came or looked for either flattery or money from them (2:5–6). In this, Paul was comparing himself to the false teachers whose *modus operandi* was to lure believing Gentiles into their net with flattery, and then, after maneuvering themselves into positions of superiority over them, to receive from believing Gentiles the financial support that rightfully belonged to true men of God.

2Thessalonians

In this letter, Paul warned the saints that a great apostasy was coming (2:3) because of a lack of love for the truth among believers (2:10–12). In fact, he said, the apostasy had already begun (2:7). It should also be emphasized again that every instance of Paul *not* mentioning circumcision or the law bore weight with Gentile saints. It was helpful to the Thessalonians for Paul to say only that Jesus would mete out punishment to those who did not know God and to those who did not obey the gospel (1:8), making no mention of punishment for those who did not keep the law. Of course, by "the gospel", Paul meant the gospel he preached to the Gentiles, not the gospel given to Peter for the Jews.

Romans

The matter of circumcision and the law occupied much of Paul's attention in this letter to the saints in Rome. In it, Paul addressed both Jewish and Gentile believers, which tells us there was close contact between the two groups in Rome. Indeed, there may not have been two groups at all, but one Assembly, comprised of both Jews and Gentiles. This would be possible as long as both groups followed after the Spirit, for nothing in the Spirit would lead to strife between them. Paul's letter does suggest, however, that some degree of friction existed, for he exhorted the Jews, who were forbidden to eat certain foods, not to despise the Gentiles who were free to eat, and he exhorted the Gentiles, who were free to eat any food, not to condemn their Jewish brothers who could not eat (14:3). Likewise with the holy days: "One man regards one day above another, but another man regards every day alike. Let each be fully persuaded in his own mind. He who observes the day [the Jew], observes it to the Lord, and he who does not observe the day [the Gentile], to the Lord he does not observe it" (14:5–6a). And then Paul asked them all a penetrating question: "Why do you condemn your [Jewish] brother? Or why do you despise your [Gentile] brother? For we shall all stand before the judgment seat of Christ" (14:10). Paul made it perfectly clear that there was no cause for either Jews or Gentiles to be proud of their earthly condition. As he told the Galatians, "In Christ Jesus, neither circumcision nor uncircumcision is worth anything [to God], but faith expressed through love."[435]

In chapter two of this letter, Paul made as radical a statement as he ever made: "[To God,] one is not a Jew outwardly; nor is circumcision

---

[435] Gal. 5:6.

outward in the flesh. But one is a Jew inwardly, and circumcision is of the heart, by the Spirit, not the letter, whose praise is not of men, but of God" (2:28–29). That statement would have gotten Paul stoned in Jerusalem, but he felt free to write plainly to the Roman Assembly. He wrote, "Circumcision is indeed profitable if you observe the law, but if you are a transgressor of the law, your circumcision is made uncircumcision. If, therefore, the uncircumcision keep the righteousness of the law, shall not his uncircumcision be counted as circumcision? And shall not the one in the natural state of uncircumcision who fulfills the law judge you who with the letter and circumcision are a transgressor of the law?" (2:25–27). "So then, we conclude that a man is made righteous by faith, without works of the law. Is He God of the Jews only? Is He not also God of the Gentiles? Yes, of the Gentiles, too, seeing that there is one God" (3:28–30a).

Paul acknowledged the blessings that came with being an Israelite (9:4–5), not the least of which was that the Messiah was sent to minister only to the nation of Israel (15:8). He insisted, however, that "not everyone who is from Israel is Israel" (9:6), for God does not consider everyone who is physically descended from Abraham to be a child of Abraham, but only the one who believes in His Son and has received the promise of the Spirit. "That is to say, the children of the flesh, these are not the children of God, but the children of the promise are counted as the seed" (9:7–8). Paul does not state his reasons for bringing these things up, but those reasons certainly existed. At the least, his mention of God's unique blessings on Israel helped believing Gentiles to avoid becoming puffed up against their Jewish brothers, and his warnings to Israel helped them maintain a godly attitude toward their Gentile brothers.

The wisdom Paul demonstrated in his explanation of Abraham's faith is arresting. Paul wrote, "If Abraham were justified by works [ceremonial rites], he had something of which to boast" (4:2). Then, quoting Genesis 15:6, he continued by saying that Abraham simply "believed God, and it was reckoned to him as righteousness" (4:3). And he made the astute observation that Abraham received circumcision *after* this event, which forces the conclusion that God counted Abraham righteous *before* he was circumcised and that Abraham received circumcision only as "a seal of the righteousness of the faith that he had while in uncircumcision, that he might be the father of all who believe" (4:11).

1Corinthians

The issue of the law and Peter's gospel did not play a large role in Paul's first letter to the Corinthians, but it is present. In both letters, Paul ridiculed false teachers for coming behind him, building upon the foundation he had laid in Corinth instead of winning their own converts to Christ (1Cor. 3:10–15; 2Cor. 10:13–16). What the false teachers were teaching, we are not told, but Paul's jealousy of the Corinthians' growing faith in those teachers compelled him to remind them of who he was to them in Christ: "*You* may have countless tutors in Christ, but not many fathers, for in Christ Jesus, I have begotten *you* through the gospel" (4:15).

1Timothy

Late in his life, Paul left his trusted young protégé, Timothy, in Ephesus to help that Assembly (1:3). Paul would rather have had Timothy travel with him, but matters were deteriorating in the region, and Paul hoped that Timothy might stem the tide of apostasy. Paul began this first letter to Timothy by referring to those in Ephesus who had "turned aside to empty talk, desiring to be teachers of the law, but understanding neither what they say nor the things they so confidently assert" (1:5–7). "The law is good," Paul wrote, but only "if a man uses it lawfully" (1:8). These Gentiles did not know how to "use it lawfully" because it was contrary to the will of God for them to use the law at all.

Real situations motivated Paul to give the instruction he gave; he did not run his race aimlessly or throw punches at the air (1Cor. 9:26). Therefore, if Paul reminded Timothy that there is but "one Mediator between God and men – the man Christ Jesus" (2:5) – then someone must have been trying to persuade the Ephesians that there was another mediator between them and God – whether Moses or Israel's high priest, Paul does not say.

How concerned Paul was that his converts were being turned from his gospel is indicated by the fact that he even felt the need to plead with Timothy, "I was ordained a preacher, an apostle – I am speaking the truth in Christ! I am not lying – a faithful and true teacher of Gentiles" (2:7). The mythological Paul of Christianity would never have felt the need to do that, for the status of that Paul among believers was unshakable. However, the real Paul, knowing that he was losing the respect of the body of Christ, had to abase himself to defend his calling and authority in Christ. He wrote Timothy as he did in order to protect the young minister's heart from the slander that Paul was sure Timothy was hearing. Especially important was this warning Paul gave him: "Do not receive an accusation against an elder, except in the presence of two or three witnesses" (5:19). In other words, "Do not listen to anything against me when you are alone." Paul knew that slanderers operate effectively only when their victims are unprotected by openness.

Paul prophesied that an apostasy of the body of Christ was coming "in the latter times" (4:1–3), but his closing words to Timothy show that he was aware that a downward spiral in the body of Christ had already begun: "O Timothy, guard the deposit;[436] avoid the worthless, empty talk and contradictions of that which is falsely called knowledge, which by professing, some have deviated from the faith" (6:20–21).

Titus

To Titus, who was on the island of Crete (1:5), Paul wrote, "There are many rebellious, vain talkers and deceivers, especially those of the circumcision, whose mouths must be stopped." At that time, believers met in houses; therefore, when Paul said that these deceivers "subvert whole houses" (1:11a), he meant that they were deceiving whole congregations, "teaching things they should not for the sake of base gain" (1:11b). Paul exhorted Titus to "sternly rebuke" the saints on Crete so that they would remain sound in the faith and "give heed neither to Jewish myths nor to commandments of men [Gentile believers] who turn away from the truth" (1:14). Paul also warned Titus not to be drawn into worthless discussions by "foolish questions, and genealogies, and strifes, and disputes about the law" (3:9).

Paul's summary of the teaching of the false teachers was this: "They profess to know God, but by works, they deny Him" (1:16a). By saying those men were denying the Lord with "works", Paul meant ceremonial works, for by adding ceremonial rites to the Faith, the false teachers denied Christ's unique power to save. Paul explained to Titus that when God's love for humanity was revealed, it was revealed in the fact that "He delivered us by the washing of the holy Spirit . . . not by works of righteousness which we have done" (3:5). Those "works of righteousness" were the rites commanded by Moses' law,[437] and when the Spirit came, it exposed that kind of righteousness to be "like a filthy garment", just as the prophet Isaiah once said.[438] God's kind of righteousness is given to man

---

[436] "The deposit" is a reference to God's gift of the holy Spirit. Cp. 2Cor.1:22; 5:5; Eph. 1:14.

[437] Dt. 6:25.

[438] Isa. 64:6.

by the Spirit, not by the law, and by the Spirit alone are men justified with God and have hope of eternal life (3:6–7).

2Timothy

In his first letter, Paul exhorted Timothy to warn the saints in Ephesus not to give heed to myths (1Tim. 1:4). Now, in this second letter, the weary man of God predicted that the body of Christ would be turned over to myths by the God whom they were forsaking in droves, revealing to Timothy both the process and the reason for their apostasy. He wrote, "The time will come when they will not put up with sound doctrine, but will heap up teachers for themselves according to their own lusts, having itching ears, and they will turn away from hearing the truth, and they will be turned over to myths" (4:3–4). This is reminiscent of what he wrote to the Thessalonians, predicting the apostasy: "They did not receive the love of the truth so that they might be saved. And because of that, God shall send to them a strong delusion so that they will believe the lie, that they all might be damned who did not believe the truth, but took pleasure in unrighteousness" (2Thess. 2:10–12).

It was in this second letter to Timothy, written from prison, that Paul made the astonishing, heart-breaking comment, "You know this, that all they in Asia have forsaken me" (1:15). Timothy certainly did know it, for he was in Asia at that time, in the city of Ephesus, striving with all his youthful might to save what was left of the Assembly in that city. Knowing the difficulties Timothy was facing, Paul exhorted him to "maintain the standard of sound words which you have heard from me" (1:13), and "be strong in the grace that is in Christ Jesus", and "patiently endure hardship as a good soldier of Jesus Christ" (2:1, 3). Paul reminded this godly young minister that "all who are willing to live godly in Christ Jesus will be persecuted" (3:12), and that he himself was enduring the hardship of prison life so that his gospel would survive to benefit others (2:8–10).

Paul saw that if ceremonial rites were allowed into the Assembly, they would eventually replace the saints' dependence upon the Spirit, and he warned Timothy not to associate with those who were taking that path (3:5). Paul knew that once the flesh had its way, intellectualism would replace revelation (3:7) and that human credentials, such as "letters of recommendation", would replace the divine credentials of spiritual power and gifts. By the time of this second letter, those who taught Peter's gospel included many Gentiles whom Paul himself had once taught, and he compared such apostates to those who rebelled against Moses in the wilderness, saying, "Like Jannes and Jambres, who withstood Moses, so

these men also withstand the truth, men whose minds are corrupt, repro-
bate concerning the faith" (3:8). During his last visit with the elders of
Ephesus, Paul forewarned them that this would happen, saying, "After my
departure, vicious wolves will come in among you, not sparing the flock.
Even from among your own selves shall men rise up, speaking perverse
things in order to draw away disciples after themselves. Therefore, be on
guard, and remember that for three years, night and day, I did not cease
from exhorting each one of you with tears."[439]

Paul left no stone unturned in his effort to save Timothy from being
corrupted while he ministered in the region where apostasy had become
the new norm for God's people. He reminded Timothy of the faith of his
mother and grandmother (1:5). He reminded him of his greatest source of
strength: "Stir up the gift of God which is in you through the laying on of
my hands!" (1:6). He told Timothy of his constant prayers on his behalf
(1:3), and of his desire to see him (1:4), and he appealed to Timothy's
deep love for him by begging him not to be "ashamed of the witness of
our Lord, nor of me, his prisoner" (1:8).

2Corinthians

By the time Paul penned his second letter to the Corinthian Assembly,
they had suffered such a drastic downturn in their spiritual condition that
Paul pleaded with them to be reconciled again to God (5:20). False teachers had persuaded many of the Assemblies to adopt a system in which
only ministers who carried letters of recommendation would be received.
Paul was incensed. "Is it that we need, as some do, letters of recommendation to *you*, or recommendations from *you*? *You* yourselves are our letter!" (3:1–2a).

Paul was especially disappointed that when the teachers of Peter's
gospel slandered Paul in Corinth, the Corinthians did not stand up for him.
If the Corinthians had stood up for Paul against the false teachers, they
might have overcome the temptation to turn to their Jewish gospel, but
because they did not, the false teachers' slander had taken root and was
growing. Paul repeatedly stressed to the Corinthians that they should
have stood up for him against his detractors "because we are *your* boasting, as *you* are ours, in the day of the Lord Jesus" (1:14). Their failure to
uphold Paul put him in the unwanted position of having to speak up for
himself (5:12), and doing so made Paul feel foolish: "I have done foolish-
ly in boasting, but *you* compelled me. For my recommendation ought to

---

[439] Acts 20:29–31.

have come from *you*, for in nothing am I inferior to these super-apostles, although I am nothing" (12:11; 10:8; 11:16–19).

Paul was deeply hurt by the erosion of the Corinthian Assembly's trust in him, and he ridiculed their new-found confidence in their circumcised leaders with their ceremonial forms: "Since many are boasting according to the flesh, I, too, will boast. . . . Are they Hebrews? So am I. Are they Israelites? So am I. Are they seed of Abraham? So am I. Are they ministers of Christ? (I am talking like a madman.) I am more!" (11:18– 23a). Just as Paul was compelled to do with his other converts, he humbled himself in this letter to plead with these saints to believe him: "The God and Father of the Lord Jesus Christ, He who is praised forever, knows that I am not lying" (11:31). Finally, after boasting of his Jewish pedigree the way the false teachers had done, Paul refused to boast any more about anything except what Jesus had done for him by the Spirit (11:30; 12:1–10).

Apparently, false teachers had suggested to the Corinthians that Paul was out of his mind, to which slander Paul offered this: "If we be out of our mind, it is to God, or if we be in our right mind, it is to *you*" (5:13). They had also suggested that Paul's teaching and authority were of his own will, not of the will of God (10:2), that Paul wrote pompously authoritative letters (10:9), and that he was an unskilled orator (11:6) – the last accusation bearing great weight in that culture, in which orators were highly esteemed. As a result, Paul was again reduced to begging his converts to love him (6:13) and to see that his gospel was not holding them back, but that it had liberated them to walk in fellowship with the true God (6:12).

The mythological Paul of Christianity never had to defend himself and to beg the saints whom he had brought to Christ to receive him, but the real Paul wrote this: "Receive us! We have wronged no one; we have corrupted no one; we have taken advantage of no one" (7:2). Sadly, their memory of the blessings which Paul had brought them was so darkened by the slander of false teachers that now, after all the years they had known Paul, they were in doubt concerning his authenticity as an apostle of Christ. Though deeply hurt and disappointed, Paul was not cowed: "If I come again, I will not spare, since *you* desire proof of Christ speaking in me. . . . I expect that *you* will find that we are not reprobates" (13:2b–3a, 6).

Paul condemned the false teachers for promoting themselves and preaching themselves (3:1; 4:5; 10:18) and for taking donations from the Corinthian saints for their ministry, accusing them of "peddling the word of God" (2:17). Years before this, Paul foresaw that such men would come and subvert the Corinthians' faith, and he determined to make a difference between those teachers and himself by refusing to take any money from his converts in this region. "Did I commit a sin in humbling myself so that *you* might be exalted, in that I preached the gospel of God to *you* without charge? I robbed other Assemblies, taking wages from them in order to serve *you*. And when I was there with *you*, and in need, I was not a burden to anyone, for when the brothers from Macedonia came, they fully supplied my need, and I kept myself, and I will keep myself in every way, from being burdensome to *you*. As the truth of Christ is in me, this boasting of mine shall not be silenced in the regions of Achaia" (11:7–10).

Paul did not regret how much it had cost him to have refused financial support from the Corinthians. "Most gladly", he said, "will I spend and be spent for *your* souls, although the more I love *you*, the less I am loved" (12:15). And he begged them, with great irony, to forgive him for taking such good care of their souls: "In what way were *you* less privileged than the rest of the Assemblies, except that I was not burdensome to *you*? Forgive me this wrong" (12:13). By refusing their financial support, Paul had set himself up to be able to say, in effect, "Let those men love *you* the way I have loved *you*." That is to say, "Let those men teach *you* their gospel for free, as I have done." Paul knew those teachers would never do so, for he knew their hearts, that they were ministering for their own gain. "Such men are pseudo-apostles, deceitful workers, masquerading as apostles of Christ. And no wonder, for Satan disguises himself as a messenger of light. Therefore, it is no great thing if his ministers also disguise themselves as ministers of righteousness, whose end shall be according to their works" (11:13–15).

The most telling comment Paul made in this letter concerning the spiritual condition of the body of Christ as a whole is the grim comment he made after listing the things he had suffered for the gospel. Beyond his physical sufferings, Paul said, he was burdened with "daily insurrection against me, the concern for all the Assemblies" (11:28). This heart-rendng statement, that Paul was daily concerned about insurrection among his converts everywhere, reveals that the apostasy was already widespread.

Evidence of the Apostasy from the Other Apostles

In his latter years, John was also witness to the apostasy which broke Paul's heart, for it affected the Assembly to which John himself belonged. John knew much but wrote little, preferring to speak face-to-face with the saints to whom he ministered (2Jn. 1:12; 3Jn. 1:13). Consequently, he left only a few statements that show the contempt in which he was held by apostate believers. However, the few words John left us provides additional biblical evidence that in his latter years, this beloved apostle became *persona non grata* in some Assemblies. "I wrote to the Assembly," John said in one case, "but Diotrephes, who likes to be chief among them, does not receive us . . . . disparaging us with evil words" (3Jn. 1:9–10a). Such was no doubt the attitude of other pastors as well, for John, like Paul, said that "many" had fallen away from the truth (1Jn. 2:18; cp. 2:26). It is impossible that John alone, of all Jesus' original apostles, was unwelcome in some Assemblies. When John said that "Diotrephes does not receive *us*," he was referring to Diotrephes' rejection of John and of any who had fellowship with him.

Paul and John were part of a faithful remnant of the body of Christ, and the fact that the faithful were forsaken by "all" (Paul), and rejected by "many" (John), confirms that by the end of the apostles' lives, the body of Christ as a whole had fallen into apostasy.

No more convincing confirmation of the pervasiveness of the apostasy exists than the boldness of the men who were its ministers. Such heights of arrogance against the apostles of Christ could never have been scaled without the support of a multitude. By the time of John's letter, then, it is obvious that many congregations were being led by ministers like Diotrephes, which would account for the audacity of such ministers: "He doesn't receive the brothers, and he forbids those who would, and expels them from the Assembly" (3Jn. 1:10b). Christianity's mythological John would never have been denied entrance into an Assembly of believers, but the real John was. And in such an atmosphere, it is easy to understand why John would say that his greatest joy was to hear that his children in Christ were still walking in the truth (3Jn. 1:4; 2Jn. 1:4).

While the chief focus of the letters from Peter, James, John, and Jude was on moral instruction, all of them touched on the issue of the apostasy. Peter prophesied that, emboldened by multitudes of deluded believers, false teachers such as Diotrephes would lead many astray and cause the truth to be spoken against (2Pet. 2:1–2). James' Jewish roots came through very clearly in his letter; still, he emphasized being born of the Spirit rather than a fleshly, Jewish birth (1:18), and he spoke with reverence of a law that is higher than the law of Moses, calling it "the perfect law of liberty" (1:25; 2:12) and "the royal law" (2:8).

James' contention that Abraham was justified by works (2:21–24) has been badly misconstrued by many Christian teachers as contradicting

Paul's gospel of liberty from works. But by "works", James was referring to righteous deeds, not to ceremonial rites. Paul would have agreed with James, that righteous deeds are required for salvation (e.g., Rom. 2:5–10), and James would have agreed with Paul, that Gentiles did not need the ceremonial works of the law.

As for Jude, his knowledge of the apostasy is revealed in his warning against certain "ungodly men" in the Assemblies, who were at that time ministering and worshipping among the saints without fear of God's righteous judgment (Jude 1:4, 8–19).

How Did They Do It?

Paul's converts loved Paul dearly at first. How, then, were they persuaded, *en masse*, to forsake him? The following are some of the reasons that teachers of Peter's gospel for the Jews enjoyed such great success among Gentile believers:

- Being Jewish, the false teachers had immediate status among believing Gentiles after those Gentiles learned that the God of the Jews was the only true God. Jesus himself was a Jew, and God had given that nation the law and the prophets.
- Some false teachers would have known the apostles personally, and the older ones may even have walked with Jesus.
- The false teachers may have possessed spiritual gifts and power, since that was the norm among believers of the time (cp. Acts 21:8–9; 1Cor. 12:4–11; Gal. 3:5).
- False teachers would have had a great knowledge of the Scriptures.
- The gospel of the false teachers was the gospel with which the body of Christ had begun and was the gospel that Jesus had preached and that Peter and the other apostles were still preaching.
- The false teachers could point to Paul's history of persecution of the saints, bolstering their message with stories of saints who had suffered from his cruelties.

So, those who went to the Gentile Assemblies with Peter's gospel were in a strong position. They had powerful spiritual weapons with which to assail the fortress of the Gentiles' trust in Paul. Paul was vastly outnumbered by those men, and the congregations that Paul founded throughout the Roman Empire were eventually overwhelmed by the arguments against him. The gospel that required believers to be ceremonially as well as spiritually clean won the day, and it is still winning. The fact that Paul lost his battle to establish the Gentiles in the truth means, even to this day, when someone is invited to believe the gospel that the real Paul preached, he is being invited to join the losing side, in this world. Like Jesus, Paul ended his life rejected by his own, having failed to persuade those whom he had led to Christ of the veracity of his message.

Afterword

Most believers outside of Jerusalem and Antioch would never have seen a copy of the letter which the apostles and elders at the Jerusalem Council sent to the Assembly in Antioch, and rumors of the letter would have borne insufficient weight for believers to be persuaded of it. So, in spite of the Council's decision, Paul had to spend much of his strength afterward laboring to save his Gentile converts from adding ceremonial works to the Faith. The zeal of the false teachers took them everywhere, it seems, to undo Paul's influence, and the body of Christ, in a relatively short time, fell into apostasy despite Paul's herculean efforts. Unable to be everywhere at once, Paul could not put out the multitude of fires that burned the truth out of the hearts of his converts, and after those first-century Gentiles rejected Paul's gospel in favor of Peter's, it was only a matter of time before the body of Christ degenerated into just another worldly institution. Just as Moses had foreseen the results of Israel's apostasy, Paul foresaw what would happen to the apostate body of Christ. Seeing what was certainly to come upon the apostate saints, Paul could have quoted some of Moses' last words to Israel (Dt. 31:29): "I know that after my death, *you* will utterly corrupt *yourselves* and turn aside from the way that I have commanded *you*, and that evil will befall *you* in the latter days because *you* will have done evil in the sight of the LORD, to provoke Him to anger by the work of *your* hands."

As believers drifted ever farther from Paul's gospel of the reliance solely upon the Spirit, they grew more worldly-wise, and the more worldly-wise they grew, the more ceremonial form they added to the Faith. Thus began the apostate body of Christ's journey toward acceptance by the world. And after several centuries of trial-and-error doctrinal and ceremonial development, the fallen body of Christ was so finely adorned with worldly beauty that she would attract the favorable attention of the world's master, Rome, and blend with it to become the vicious Iron Kingdom foreseen by the prophet Daniel, "which will be different from all kingdoms, and it will devour the whole earth, and it will tread it down and break it to pieces" (7:23). The apostasy of believers in the second and third centuries AD, which resulted in their blending with the Roman Empire, is the subject of the next book in The Iron Kingdom Series.

Books by John D. Clark, Sr.

—⌘—

Spiritual Light

Suffering and the Saints

The Apostate Fathers

Speaking in Tongues at Spirit Baptism

What Does the Bible Really Say About Hell?

Is the Bible the Word of God?

Marriage and Divorce

Solomon's Wisdom

God Had a Son before Mary Did

Tithes and Offerings

Malachi

After Jesus Died

The Iron Kingdom Book Series:
    Book 1: Slander
    Book 2: The Jerusalem Council
    Book 3: *Coming soon!*

—⌘—

For free book downloads visit us at:

www.GoingtoJesus.com